A True Story

A Cuban in New York

A True Story

A Cuban in New York

by Miguel Barnet

Translation by Regina Galasso

Prologue by José Manuel Prieto

Jorge Pinto Books Inc.
New York

Contents

On *A True Story* by Miguel Barnet

This is the novel of conflicting nostalgias. The human drama of always wanting to be somewhere else without ever leaving where we are. In other words, feeling devastated for having made it somewhere to end up being nowhere. For a good reason or none at all, whether we meant it or not, we Latin Americans have been both instigators and victims of this bitter and bodacious fate of parallel mirrors. Miguel Barnet has proved it to us with the burning complicity of a true story: we all are Julián Mesa, the nostalgic double of this exemplary novel.

—Gabriel García Márquez

Prologue

A Life's Memories

With the publication of *La vida real*—the original Spanish title of *A True Story*—by the poet and ethnographer Miguel Barnet (Havana, January 28th, 1940) in 1986, the series of testimonial novels, shaped by his pen, successfully carried on. The series began in 1966, when he released, at the age of 26, a book that would make history in Hispanic-American literature: *Biografía de un cimarrón* (*Biography of a Runaway Slave*).[1] The book was the result of months of interviews with Esteban Montejo, a 103-year-old ex-slave, born in 1860. Barnet had started working at the newfound Institute of Ethnography and Folklore of the Academy of Sciences of Cuba and established a close relationship with the well-known ethnographer Fernando Ortiz. He also had begun to research Afro-Cuban religion. Meeting Montejo, who was in a home for the elderly at the time, impacted him in such a way that he decided to work on a testimony about his life as a runaway slave and later as a soldier in the Cuban War of Independence. The book is one of the few slave narratives of Cuban literature and possesses astonishing immediacy and spontaneity. In numerous interviews, Barnet has told about how the ex-slave was reluctant at first to tell his story to a young man who would go visit him with a clunky tape-recorder until he himself would ask him to tape the most relevant episodes in future sessions.

The book was an immediate bestseller. It received the highest national and international critical praise. The famous English novelist Graham Greene, who is very knowledgeable about Third World literature, even said: "There wasn't a book like this before,

---

1   The work was translated into English as *The Autobiography of a Runaway Slave* (1968) by Jocasta Innes, and later as *Biography of a Runaway Slave* (1994) by W. Nick Hill.

and it is quite improbable it will be repeated." *Biography of a Runaway Slave* also motivated the famous composer Hans Werner Henze to create a triumphant opera whose libretto was written by Hans Magnus Enzensberger.

Barnet became a literary celebrity. From that point on, readers greatly anticipated the release of his books. It took Barnet four years to publish his next book *Canción de Rachel* (*Rachel's Song*), another testimonial novel about the life of a Cuban starlet, who was also elderly when Barnet interviewed her.[2] The book was not as enthusiastically received, perhaps, because Barnet incorporated several voices. Different from a monologue, like his earlier *Biography of a Runaway Slave* (and the book you are holding), *Rachel's Song* is a dialogue of several life narratives. However, the book did also meet considerable audience success and was taken to the big screen. The film *La bella del Alhambra*, inspired by this novel, was a real cinematographic event when it was released in 1989.

In 1984, Barnet published *Gallego*, the third of his famous testimonial novels, about the life of a Spanish emigrant who arrived in Cuba from Galicia during the early years of the Republic.[3] The novel received the Literary Critics' Award and was also taken to the big screen. Finally, in 1986 the book you have in your hands was published. *A True Story* is a biography of a normal Cuban, Julián Mesa, who after an eventful life in the Cuban countryside and then in Havana, decides to emigrate to the United States a decade before the triumph of the Cuban Revolution. This book, now out for the first time in English, 26 years after its publication in Spanish, has been translated into numerous other languages among which the Italian *La Vita Reale* (1997) and the German *Ein Kubaner in New York* (1990) editions are worth highlighting.

Barnet is also the author of fine poetical work, which includes book titles like *La piedra fina y el pavorreal* (1966), *La sagrada familia* (1967), and *Mapa del tiempo* (1989). It is pertinent to mention

---

2 *La canción de Rachel* was translated into English by W. Nick Hill as *Rachel's Song* in 1991.

3 This novel is not yet available in English.

his poetry because it explains, I think, the secret of his success with biographies. From being a poet, he gets the meticulous literary production, the accuracy of his prose, that blending of scientific rigor and exquisite imagination. The exceptional literary finish of his work is particularly relevant to *A True Story* and also distinguishes it from similar texts such as Oscar Lewis's famous *The Children of Sánchez: Autobiography of a Mexican Family* (1961).[4] The ethnographic account achieves the dignity of a literary work in Barnet's writing, where others only see a scientific report. Barnet said: "With *Biography of a Runaway Slave*, I made a critical edition, a book that didn't have anything comparable in Cuban literature. It was foreign, hybrid, with a prologue, substantial notes, an epilogue, and a glossary" (Interview 101).

When the Spanish edition of *Rachel's Song* was published, Barnet deemed it necessary to add a long essay in which he explained the key principals of what he called the documentary novel. Since it is extremely illuminating to understand how his books have been written, it is worth considering this long quote:

> In a documentary novel spoken discourse is the fundamental trait of the language, the only way it takes on life. But it must be a recreated spoken language, not a mere reproduction of what was on tape. From the recording I take the tone, the anecdotes, the inflexions; the rest, the style and fine points, I add myself. A book like Oscar Lewis' *La Vida* is a great contribution to the psychology and sociology of marginalized masses. It is, simply and plainly: I write what you tell me and in the way you tell me. Lewis' approach has little to do with the documentary novels I write. To my way of thinking, literary imagination should go hand in hand with sociological imagination. A documentary novelist should give free rein to his or her imagination, so long as it does not distort the protagonist's character or betray his

---

4   *The Children of Sánchez* was originally published in English in 1961 followed by a Spanish translation of it in 1964 by Fondo de Cultura Económica.

or her language. Imagination, invention within a realistic essence, is the only way a writer can get the most out of a given phenomenon. In *Rachel*, for example, I say: "This is her story, her life as she told it to me and as I later told it back to her." Many things are implicit in that statement. Written memory is not a spontaneous recollection. ("The Documentary Novel" 25)

In a recent speech delivered in Santiago de Chile upon receiving the José Donoso Iberoamerican Award of Arts and Literature, Barnet stated that "more than creating, more than inventing, what I have done in my prose is recreate, even reinvent a tradition that was going to die, acting as a resonator of voices, making figures appear through their own luminosity who were drowning in the opaque" ("Palabras" 310).

The voice that resonates in *A True Story* belongs to Julián Mesa. The novel is about a mestizo peasant who has lived a life of the profoundest poverty. Here I certainly see Lewis's influence on the Cuban's work. Barnet finds his informants among society's poorest in the vein of Lewis's interest in "the culture of poverty." But Barnet has the ability to organize the narration in a way that makes real life appear dramatically organized like a novel. There are moments when it seems like a story told by an inhabitant of Macondo, the mythic hamlet of Gabriel García Márquez. In that sense, the first part of the book is a profoundly Caribbean story that could have occurred in any of the region's countries. It provides shocking details: the many hours of labor, the exhausting work with sugarcane, the abuse by the plantation owners and overseers. All of them greatly recall Márquez's fiction. It must not be forgotten that the years are the same. And the landscape: "Sugarcane fields, lowlands, banana plantations, a sorry excuse for a river, and misery, misery, and more misery."

Another totally Macondian detail is Julián's rather childish fascination with the circus, where he ends up working. It becomes, like many things in his story, a gauge by which he measures everything later on in his life. The entire book happens like a flash back. It is a recount of Mesa's life told from New York. Many years later, in

New York, where he is interviewed, he says: "I'll never forget the circus. When I got to see the big circuses, the ones with two and three rings, I was disappointed. There weren't any rumba dancers or fire-eaters. And no *Blackaman*. For me the real circus . . . is the circus from the countryside towns."

A True Story is also commendable for the true gallery of memorable characters Julián meets on his journey. Aside from the main character, with whom the reader has the chance to become friends, the novel is full of very well defined characters: Horacio, the heartless town tycoon who builds up the circus; Eva la Libanesa, his neighbor in a poor apartment building in Havana; and his unforgettable friend Miguelito, with whom he emigrates to the United States, and whose every move we carefully and sympathetically follow. Lastly, the memorable portrait of Celia, the young Puerto Rican woman he meets at a dance in El Barrio. "Her life was like a soap opera." Julián is more than twice her age and he ends up marrying her.

But besides its many literary merits, what makes *A True Story* particularly attractive and completely justifies its release in English is the meticulous, detailed, warm portrait of the Hispanic community, the world of El Barrio during the 50s. "El Barrio looked like a circus. It's the same today. . . . Miguelito and I both thought El Barrio was the most entertaining place in New York." It includes everything: the dances he would go to, the musicians who made a living any way they could and dreamed of being hits on Broadway, the endless conversations in the barbershops. With the publication of this book, I do not think that any account of New York's Latino world during that period can ignore it: *A True Story* is destined to become a mandatory reference.

The original Spanish title *La vida real* is a parody of Lewis's book *La vida: A Puerto Rican Family in the Culture of Poverty*, published in New York in 1965, which describes the same environment. Barnet parodies it and corrects it: he adds the adjective "*real*" to the title. The picture he draws, he wants to let us know, fully surpasses the work of the American author because of the richness in detail and, most of all, its emotional impact. Barnet must have wanted to settle the old polemic about his indebtedness to Lewis, or as the title of the interview published in *Revista Anual de Ciencias Sociales* states: "Not an Epigone of Oscar Lewis or Truman Capote." However, in the interview, Barnet does state his indebtedness to a writer who had been the first to use the method of the testimonial novel at least one decade before he did. He refers to the Mexican ethnologist Ricardo Pozas, author of the memorable book *Pérez Jolote: Biografía de un tzotzil* (*Juan the Chamula: An Ethnological Re-creation of the Life of a Mexican Indian*), published in Mexico in 1952. Barnet says: "The presence of Don Ricardo Pozas, who was my teacher, our teacher, in the 60s impacted me a great deal" (100).[5]

The whole first "Cuban" part of *A True Story*—which might seem less attractive to the English-speaking reader—is, nevertheless, indispensable to understanding something essential about this book and its main character: the biographical substratum, more than anything the full life left behind by any emigrant in this city. What happened before prevents him from letting everything dissolve in his new environment and becomes, as I previously mentioned, the gauge, the basis for comparison, which he uses for all his experiences in the United States, his new country.

Julián Mesa refuses to lose his identity: "One of the things that really caught my attention when I got here was Cuban *guajiros* from Mayarí . . . who gave themselves a name like Frank, Mike, or Tony. Or they'd change their last name like a Park Avenue doorman, named Guillermo Guerra, who had the nerve to call himself Billy Battle." This anecdote not only provides clear evidence of the psychological pressure felt by an emigrant to assimilate to the dominant culture, to evaporate in the famous melting pot, but also shows us a person who's proud of his culture, his roots. For Julián there was never any doubt: "When they say to me: 'Cuban-American?' I say: 'No. Only Cuban.'"

—José Manuel Prieto

---

5   The English translation by Lysander Kemp was published in 1962.

Works Cited

Barnet, Miguel. "The Documentary Novel." *Cuban Studies/ Estudios Cubanos* 11 (1981): 19–32.

———. Interview with Yanko González. "Ni épigono de Oscar Lewis ni de Truman Capote." *Revista Austral de Ciencias Sociales* 13 (2007): 93–109.

———. "Palabras de agradecimiento al recibir el Premio Iberoamericano de Letras 'José Donoso' 2007." *Revista UNIVERSUM* 23:1 (2008): 309–11.

Introduction

Every human life is important. However, some lives have more outstanding characteristics than others. The life of a Hispanic emigrant in New York is one of them. Until now, I haven't come across a single work that shows Cuban emigrants' feelings of pain and dissatisfaction in the North. Unfortunately, the most common parameters to describe the life of Hispanic emigrants in general have been overly abstract models of culture and stereotyped ways of living. Not totally convinced by these generalizations, I opted to write a book that shows the heart of this human conglomerate, which is sometimes totally covered up and other times capriciously manipulated.

With *A True Story*, I don't aim to present a definitive and totalizing picture of Cuban emigration of the 40s and 50s. The contrasts and differences among those emigrants are too bold to try to comprise an all-embracing entirety. I've chosen a living character among many. Perhaps he's not representative of such a vast and motley social phenomenon, but he does contain a general importance in terms of historical fate.

Memory as part of the imagination has been the touchstone of this book. If I've recreated dramatic situations and true characters, it's been in total harmony with the fundamental key of all my testimonial work. I haven't adulterated contexts nor betrayed the oral (confessional) discourse of my informants. On the contrary, I've even respected the linguistic turns of those who position themselves in front of the microphone of a tape recorder with certain rhetorical seriousness as if dictating a novel. I believe that an undeniable aesthetic value is also part of that tone. We've conversed, however, in a close and creative give-and-take.

Testimony has always served as the novel's documentary appoggiatura. On the flipside, I make clear that I'm not a novelist through and through. If I'm on the fence between anthropological and literary tendencies, it's because I believe that it's about time they go hand in hand without rejecting each other. Conversely, I'm convinced that they complement one another. I don't propose categorical definitions, nor offer social solutions. I only wish to show a man's heart. The one belonging to the man who middle-class historiography stamped with proverbial fatalism, inscribing him among "the people without history." This is the case of Julián Mesa, another Cuban from the infinite mass of emigrants who abandoned their Island in search of a better life. His integration in New York's Hispanic world, his conjugal link with a woman of Puerto Rican origin, his social permeability, his forms of expression acquired through reading and the clash with a new culture didn't distance him from his patriotic roots.

I hope this book illustrates that the lives of men of the so-called culture of poverty don't always lack a will to live, a historical consciousness. Even when they are anchored in a feeling of marginality, the flame of life flickers towards the future.

Because of his dramatic personal experience, José Martí wrote, "You can't make a home in a foreign land." Julián Mesa echoes this statement. And he adds: "For me to talk about Cuba is like talking about a person. In fact, I've never really left there."

Here you have the gist of this book, its essential message. As a provincial professor would say, the rest is "life's fallen leaves."

—Miguel Barnet

Acknowledgements

Miguel Barnet

I thank the Center for Cuban Studies and the Center of Puerto Rican Studies in New York, as well as the John Simon Guggenheim Memorial Foundation for making it possible to carry out this project.

Regina Galasso

This project has roots in my first visit to Havana in 2003 when I met Miguel Barnet. I am grateful to Miguel for introducing me to this novel. I would like to especially thank Eduardo González, Fifi González, and José Manuel Prieto for sharing their knowledge of Cuba with me. Alejandro Armengol, Margaret Carson, Charles Hatfield, Gregory Horvath, LuAnn Lupia, Claudio Iván Remeseira, Oneida Sánchez, The Johns Hopkins Cuba Exchange Program, The Professional Staff Congress of the City University of New York Research Award Program, and the Borough of Manhattan Community College (CUNY) have all contributed in some way to this translation. I also thank my family, and especially Albert Lloret for love, support, and encouragement. I dedicate this translation to the memory of my grandparents.

The Countryside

When things look bad, they're only going to get worse.

Each person is a separate universe. There are some people who are born with it all planned out for them, and there are others, like myself, who go with the wind. My life has been filled with comings and goings. That's why I want peace and quiet now, although deep down I really do love adventures. To tell the truth, I've let myself be swept away by the tide. I have no regrets. What's done is done. And I'm okay with it.

When I look back and think about what's happened to me, the people I've met, all the times I've gone hungry and been in danger, I realize that life has taught me everything I need to know. Life is all there is. I was born into danger and fear means nothing to me.

Fire has always followed my footprints. And if it weren't for my mother, I wouldn't be telling this story now—a true story, not some tall tale. You could supposedly see the flames from over three hundred miles away. The fire was coming in through the cracks of our thatched roofed *bohío* and my mother was smothering them with blankets and old towels. It was a hellish roar. Gusts of hot air were burning her skin. I was three months old. She went crazy with those rags trying to stop the fire and to keep the flames from reaching the bed where I was sleeping. Then, when she smelled burnt hair and realized that it was her own, she ran over to the bed and grabbed me. Like a madwoman she ran out screaming around the entire hamlet with me in her arms, "My house! My house!" but no one heard her because most of the neighbors in the *cuartón* were in the same situation.

That's why I say I was born into danger and fear means nothing to me. But, to be honest, I always do get goose bumps when I think about that fire in the forest. Burning sugarcane is a terrible sight because the straw crackles and the flames clash with one another. When my father arrived at the clearing where we were all gathered—my mother, the neighbors, my aunts and uncles, friends and family, the whole *cuartón*—the only thing he said was "Holy shit, Fefa. You saved the kid!"

My mother would always tell me that story so I'd understand how my father felt about me. It was a real fondness that could only belong to a father. And he never hid it. My sister and brother were born—first Yara and then Pascual—and he just kept paying attention to me. He'd give me little wooden horses and rifles, and *yarey* palm-leaf hats. Everything was for me. When my sister and brother were grown up my father took off one day with a woman from Pozo Prieto. He was gone for about a month. They say he had a kid with her, and a bunch of other stuff. So one night, while my sister and brother were asleep, my mother grabbed the kerosene lamp and went to look for him. She was shaking as usual. She got to the house where he lived with that woman, knocked on the door and said to him, "Jacinto, your son Julián has a fever and won't stop calling you."

The woman burst out screaming. She was yelling his name, begging him not to go, pulling on his shirt. She even hit him. But he paid no attention and followed my mother back home. He went in the house without saying a word. He covered my head with a towel, picked me up, and ran with me in his arms for over twelve miles. I was dying of the worst sickness I've ever had: typhus.

They cured me with sulfur and rags with starch. They disinfected the house, put up a yellow flag outside, and took my sister and brother to my father's friends' place. The *curandera*, or the folk healer, and my mother saved my life. And the woman who had taken my father away never got another glimpse of him. He didn't go looking for love outside our house anymore. And even though he only had three children with my mother, wagging tongues say I really have twenty-four siblings.

In the countryside you never really know. People know how to keep secrets. It's true that he wasn't around a lot and after a while he'd come back all dressed up and give out candies and toys. And he'd bring us calendars with saints on them. Sometimes I'd ask my mother about him because he wasn't around or because I missed the gifts. She'd say to me, "The owner of the house is working, Son."

She wouldn't say "your father." That led me to believe they were never at peace. We lived close to a sugarcane field in the heart of the harvest. There was a constant odor of syrup from the boilers. Even the rice we ate was laced with the sweet flavor from the aroma that came from the sugar mill. In the dead season, the workers would go look for gigs in other places. That's when he'd disappear.

"You like the dead season, don't you, Jacinto Mesa?!"

"You don't know what you're talking about, Woman!"

"Yes, I do, Jacinto. Oh yes, I do."

"Don't you understand? I'm the owner of the house. I'm the one who brings home the money. Now tell me something: When wasn't there a plate of black beans on the table?"

"Your children and I have barely gotten by. And you know it. Don't play dumb."

And that wasn't unusual! There were months in my house when we'd only eat rice with roasted maize and parboiled sweet potatoes. And if you killed livestock, that'd mean taking away a liter of milk from my sister and brother. In the countryside, bartering was how peasants got through tough times.

Now I want to tell about how I got out of being named Cayetano, the ugliest name in the world. They called my mother Fefa but she was really Endulfa, much worse than Cayetano. But at least

Fefa was her nickname. It was easier to say and very popular in the countryside. My grandfather's name was Cayetano. He was a half mulatto *guajiro*. He was very hardworking, but dumb as a doornail. And they wanted to brand me with his name. When I was born on August 20, 1920, the first thing that mom said was: "We'll name him after his grandfather."

When the midwife saw me, she said I was the spitting image of him. The name was perfect. But luck and hunger saved my life. Since they didn't have clothes for me, my father turned to his supervisor to ask for some money to get diapers and provisions. And when the man came to see me in that makeshift bed where they'd put me, he said: "I want to baptize this child."

So, my father, who knew what he was doing, responded, "Julián, goddamn it, this is how you know who your friends are."

And no one said a single word. They forgot about Cayetano and started to call me by my godfather's name.

Back then being a godfather didn't mean you just sign a paper or go to a ceremony in a church. A godfather watched over you for the rest of your life. In the countryside saying godfather means just as much as the word brother. And brother says it all.

My sister's name is patriotic. My paternal grandmother Dolores Mesa came up with it. She'd always say, "If I have a granddaughter, she's going to be named after the Cry of Yara."

It was that simple. My younger brother Pascual got his name from Saint Paschal, the one on the insurance agency calendars. I always liked that name. It sounded happy, musical. Our family name ended with my brother since I didn't have a son. We all had the last name Mesa because we never found out who my grandfather was on my father's side. They say—and there's really no way to confirm it now that my grandmother's been dead for over fifty years—that he was an older, handsome man. He'd go by the *cuartón* on the gas car and yell at the top of his lungs, "That's where my son lives!"

My grandmother would take my father in her arms and bring him inside so my grandfather wouldn't see what was going on, or in case he wanted to take him. Rumor has it that one night he got off the gas car, squeaking his gaiters, and called out from behind the hedge of morning glories in front of the *bohío*, "Dolores, Dolores, it's me!"

My father would've been ten years old at the time, and I think that deep down he would've wanted to know who his father was. So what happened was my grandmother grabbed a recently sharpened machete and silently went out to attack him like a lioness. She slashed his shoulder and all you could hear were his squeals and strides as he ran away. She was going to hack him to death. Hack him!

I never found out the truth about what happened. But when someone in my family mentioned him, people just said "What a swine, what a swine."

What can I say about the place where I was born? Sugarcane fields, lowlands, banana plantations, a sorry excuse for a river, and misery, misery, and more misery. It was always very bleak. As a child I had no idea what a doctor was. A barber? No way! They tamed our long hair like we were beasts. And don't even ask about a movie theater or anything like it. The *batey*, where the sugarcane workers lived, next to my village was a little gem.

A few times I did get to see the circus, if that's what you can call a few scraps of tarp put together and some sickly-looking animals. Anyway, when the show came to town everyone made a big fuss about it. Everyone went. No one missed it. If you lived far away, you walked or went by wagon. You just had to get there. Even if it meant no food for a few days. I remember caravans of *guajiro* children on those muddy paths, in torrential downpours and floods, on their way to see the circus performers. It was the happiest moment of their lives.

That's how I got my globetrotter spirit. It was a very big deal to see those people do their thing in those hamlets as if they were in a plaza in the capital. They wore suits made of pieces of cheap cloth with sequins and different colored velvet. They did cartwheels non-stop. The circus sparked my imagination as a child. I saw myself trotting through villages with that gypsy troop. I always say daydreaming doesn't cost a thing. For children, dreaming is something normal they do every day. Dreaming was the only thing I could do with total freedom. To tell the truth, in my village you had to do something, anything in order to get by.

Black Man was my favorite character in the circus. We called him *Blackaman*. He hypnotized crocodiles with brandy and then put his head in their mouths. We boys would scream and cover our faces. *Blackaman* would dress in all black with a satin jacket and a leather whip. When he'd get close to the children he'd open up his big, yellow eyes as wide as he could. I'll never forget that.

The circus didn't have any young animals. They were a bunch of tired horses and monkeys that creeped you out. Sometimes they'd drag an old, gray wrinkled elephant. It was a she. A dim-wit would come by and give her a swat and she'd kick up a dust ball that would make her sneeze. Sometimes she wouldn't go in the tent. She'd only walk on flat surfaces, and at her own pace, of course. Even though you weren't supposed to give her candy, my sister and I would buy very old, hard sweets and give them to her. Telesforo sold them. He was an *isleño*, a descendent of Canary Island immigrants. He'd go around on his little mare with two saddlebags filled with goodies. Sometimes they'd be hard as rocks because they were two days old. But in the countryside, sweets were a luxury, especially for a kid.

I'll never forget the circus. When I got to see the big circuses, the ones with two and three rings, I was disappointed. There weren't any rumba dancers or fire-eaters. And no *Blackaman*. For me the real circus has a guiro drum, a kettledrum band, a tent with holes in it. It is the circus from the countryside towns. Basically for me the real thing is the poor man's circus.

In my village it was the same thing night and day: humdrum and gossip. Both cause pain, in my opinion. I've never seen working conditions anywhere else comparable to the brutality that a *guajiro* in Cuba had to put up with in those years. You were a beast of burden. During the harvest my father would come home drenched. He'd throw a bucket of water on himself and go straight to bed. He had to be up at four in the morning while it was still cool on the sugarcane plantation. Working in the sugarcane fields is tough, but once you get used to it, it's like a vice. I don't know if it's good for you or not, but he never had a bad cold or a stomachache, nothing.

He died putting out a fire in the sugarcane field. He was burnt from head to toe. The other workers were so consumed with putting out the fire that they didn't notice he'd fallen behind. The flames covered him like a blanket and he couldn't escape. In the afternoon, when there was only black smoke, they started to look for him in the burnt straw but he blended in with the land. Poor man! He was almost all ash.

That was 1932. The island was going through a tremendous depression. It was in a state of total chaos. My mother's parents took care of us. They had nothing, but at least they were family. I don't know where my mother got her strength from. Thanks to the help of the Cristinillas—our *isleña* neighbors—and Tomás Duarte, the *colono* cane farmer, we were able to get on our feet. I think about my siblings crying over my father's death and I still get all emotional. My mother didn't cry which is unusual for a woman from the countryside. But she did keep talking under her breath and once in a while we'd hear her say my father's name without rhyme or reason. I say the poor whisper what they don't let out in tears.

Lino Returrete was another *colono*. He'd go around the area on his horse and when he'd get to my house he'd ask for a coffee. "Lino's here!" he'd shout. "Where's my coffee?!"

"It's ready, it's ready! Come in, Lino," my mother would answer.

He'd leave us some change and then go get his car in the village. He was a quadroon *guajiro* with a certain look about him. My grandmother would say, "Lino is so stylish!" because he always had on cream-colored *guayaberas*, the kind the mill owners would wear. He was a little flashy. I once heard he wanted to take my mother to Manzanillo and she threatened to chop him up with a machete. I don't know the whole story, but Lino was quite a character. He surely was.

You could say we lived off the good will of others. We didn't even have any animals. My mother couldn't do a thing. And on top of that, I liked to raise pigeons. I had a pigeon loft in a mamoncillo tree. One day it caught on fire because someone wasn't careful. About seven or eight pigeons flew off in all directions. The poor things were fluttering above the tree. They were like a gray cloud with nowhere to go. They were flying and flying, looking for help. I started to cry because my pigeons were the only thing I had. I threw them some split peas so they'd eat them and then I'd be able to catch them, but they didn't go for that and they fled the area. I looked and looked for them, but they were nowhere to be found.

The poor man's misfortune struck me. The only thing I could do was work. When I was twelve, I started to break my back. I learned to read a little on my own; writing came later. It was a writing I traced or copied; no one, absolutely no one, gave me lessons until I got to Havana. It's painful if I think about that time: Ah, Cuba!

If it hadn't been for Tomás Duarte, we'd have starved to death. He's the one who got work for us on the sugar plantation. My first job was stacking sugarcane. The fun was over. My brother Pascual was in charge of the shotgun and he'd go hunting in the area around there. I never played again. My childhood ended when I carried the first stack. Just like the old black guys say, the sugar mill was the world's best invention, because you put the cane in a tube and liquid came out. I think it was oxen: without them, you'd have to toss the cartloads in the sugar mill and haul the water pipes.

In the morning, sugarcane is easy, it has some give. But when the sun is shining it's really a disaster. That's when I'd really miss my father. He was a womanizer. He liked rum. He was out a lot. He grumbled about any little thing. But he was a hardworking man. He'd work from dawn till dusk to support our family. So trying to fill his shoes when I was twelve years old, and working like a mule, was a job that was way beyond me. It was too much responsibility.

The Cristinillas sisters tried to adopt my sister. My mother gave them a big, fat N-O, although it did involve her going there to spend a few days. And my sister, the poor thing, would come back in a flash because they were constantly praying over there. They'd take her to the little church in the town every other day to confess who the hell knows what. My sister wouldn't open her mouth and Father Eugenio would say to her "Silence implies consent." She wouldn't say a thing. One day when she went to church with one of the Cristinillas sisters, the priest caught her eating candies and said to her: "With a full tummy, a Christian can't confess." My sister took it literally and when they'd put her in front of the confessional, she'd take out a cake, a banana, or a cracker. The Cristillinas girls would pinch her arm and make her say ten Our Fathers. But one night Yara snuck out of their house. She came home crying and threw herself on my mother's bed. By that time my mother was involved with Tomás Duarte.

The first months in the sugarcane field were torture. Then I got used to fresh sugar and brutality. I was only twelve and I already had muscles and a tan line on my forehead from the sombrero. In the countryside, *guajiros* are born with a sombrero on. It's the honest truth.

During the time of Sumner Welles—otherwise known as the Mediator because he arranged a shady deal with Gerardo Machado—I made twenty cents and worked twelve hours. The kettle was about to burst. The *guajiro's* salary was absurd, and the price of sugar couldn't get any lower. Deal? What deal? The stunts Machado pulled were life threatening to Cubans. It was then that the eviction notices were sent out to *guajiros* kicking them off their land. Menocal, who'd been president, tried to put together an alibi to knock down Machado, but the shot went out his ass. In Realengo 18, there was real guerilla warfare. The *guajiros* were up against the rural guard there. There was a black cloud over our heads during those years. Everywhere you looked there was nothing but devastation. It wasn't a country. When I think back I say to myself: Ah, Cuba!

Every so often a member of the Mesa family would come to my house and introduce himself: "I'm Jacinto Mesa's son."

But that didn't make things any better. My mother would let them in and if they needed a place to stay, they had one. Almost all the siblings I met were a few years older than I was. However, I heard that even up to his last days, my father was up to no good.

I don't know how people everywhere knew my maternal grand-mother. Wherever I went, I heard: "Juana la Callá, Juana la Callá." That meant "Juana the Silent One" because she had a hard time getting her words out and was embarrassed about it. She became famous for *curanderismo*. That's why so many people would come to my house. Although she lived in the *bohío* in the back, right behind ours, they'd go to my mother to ask for directions.

My grandmother was an expert at abdominal massages. For any aliment she'd give you a massage and it'd go away. Of course, if you went to her with appendicitis you wouldn't make it, but if you had indigestion or constipation, you'd leave a new man. In the countryside tapeworm was very common. *Tenia saginata* is its scientific name. My grandmother would cure it with a very potent worm-killing concoction: Tiro Seguro, or Sure Shot. Within a few days the worm would start to lose its rings and within a month the whole head would come out.

Grandma would say more with signs than words. And she'd always tell stories about spirits. She was always seeing things. And she'd hear them and get the chills and they'd tug at her legs at night. To make a long story short, she lived in a constant state of alarm. She'd say, "I'm into the Indian," and you had to know what she meant. The Indian was a plaster horseman. Every house in the countryside had one. According to her, he was a strong, protective spirit and was good for fighting. Since the Indian wore a color-ful plume on his head, my grandmother would also wear many different colors, especially green and red. "The Indian likes color," she'd say over and over again. When she was a young girl she had cut one of her braids and placed it next to the plaster figure. But one day my grandfather came home without a penny in his pocket and the devil in his body, and he grabbed the braid and burned it. When he went to grab the Indian to shatter it, she screamed, "If you break it, I'll set myself on fire!"

He ran away from the house because he knew that she was crazy about Gerónimo, the famous Indian, and that whatever she'd say she'd do, she did. But soon after my grandfather came back home with some money and a rooster, and everything was fine. In spite of his temper and everything, he was her puppet.

My grandmother would see everything: fire balls, headless horsemen, goats, suffering souls, cures, skeletons, *madres de agua*— or sea goddesses—phosphorescent lights, small Kongo people, leashed dogs, sheets, you get the point. Millions of things. Every day she'd see her father who'd been dead for 20 years. He fought in the War of Independence and then served as a soldier for the government of José Miguel Gómez. They killed him in a fight. They turned him into chopped meat. In the mornings, when she'd go out to gather wood to cook, or to get some milk, she'd see him in an anona tree. First she'd see him with the mambí machete, the kind used by Cuban insurgents who fought against Spanish troops. Then he'd be dressed in a soldier's khaki uniform, and then he'd turn into a fireball with a tail and go off, tumbling around the forest. Other times she'd see a coffin with four candles and lots of little white flowers, *brujitas* is what they're called there: that was always on the darkest of nights.

But of all my grandmother's visions, the most original, the one I liked best to hear her tell, was the one about the swamp. A dirty swamp, full of frogs and toads. No one had any reason to go there. But my grandmother would say that something would drag her there and that that magnet was God calling her as a test of faith. She could be calmly making coffee or peeling corn, but if some spirit got in her body, it would take her to the bank of the swamp. That's where she'd start to see things. The first was a *madre de agua* popping her head out and then disappearing. Then it was a man dressed in white walking on a puddle, and finally a hare with horns. For her these were all tests, tests of faith.

One day a neighbor said to her, "Juana, you can't see all that. I don't believe you." And my grandma kicked her out of the house. Another woman recommended that she hammer a rail nail to the door of her room to frighten away the dead. "I put this nail here, and no dead person will appear before me." There was no difference between her saying it and a little Kongo boy with a river elf head appearing before her. If you want to see, you see, and if you don't believe, like myself, you don't even see your own shadow.

My grandma would hardly ever talk, but between what she stuttered and what she said through gestures you could make a book of stories. After I had been living in the capital for some years, I'd run into many people from my town on the street and they'd always ask me the same thing, "Come here, Boy. Aren't you Juana la Callá's grandson?"

To see my godfather I had to walk more than three miles from my house. I'd get there barefoot with my feet hard and rough, and my tongue hanging out. I'd go because my mother would send me hoping he'd help me out a bit. He'd give me some money, that's true, but nothing out of this world, because he was basically nothing more than a supervisor and he didn't have much just like everyone else. Sometimes he'd give me a hen, a can of beans, or a pack of *rompequijadas*, hard caramel candies, and he'd call his friends to boast about his wallet. "This is Jacinto Mesa's son, but he's named after me." I'd eat more there than I would at home. And when the sun would go down, he'd put me on the railroad car and send me back without thinking twice.

Julián gave me the first pair of shoes I ever had. They were a pair of leather boots, very popular back then. They must've been a lot bigger than my size because they'd slide right on, but when I started to walk, it was living hell, I saw stars. I couldn't, I simply couldn't manage to walk with those boots on. I smeared pork lard on them, I hung them in the window, and for years I was laughed at. My brother was the only one in my house who wore shoes. My mother almost always went around barefoot. The poor woman, her feet were like claws, thorns couldn't even break her skin. That's why when I hear stories about what's going on there, and about the changes that have taken place, it makes me think. It's like a dream. A dream, yes, it's a dream, because when I think about how I was completely covered in dirt . . .

I'd get home and the first thing I'd do was shake out my hair, clean my nails with Luz Brillante, or bottled kerosene, and rub myself down with a hard bristle brush. I was a pile of dirt. My clothes always had that earthy substance of the countryside even if I washed them twenty times. I smelled like dry dirt. A crust stuck to my feet that would only come off with yellow soap and rubbing hard. Sometimes the bottoms of my feet would bleed. Since I was chubby, with a dirty face and ruddy hair, I looked like a potato. No matter how many times you'd wash yourself in the river, and fresh water does clean, that porous dirt coating never came off.

Thanks to my grandmother we weren't sick children. We had parasites, but she'd cure us right away. If we caught a cold, no problem. In the countryside, concoctions and infusions are used to cure everything. Here in New York stores that sell mostly herbs are back in fashion, naturopathy is what they call it. Now everyone uses home remedies from the beginning of time to cure themselves. It makes me laugh when I walk by those places and think about my house in the countryside, my grandmother with her little tin jar always inventing a new cure. Everything was made with herbs from the forest. She'd gather them in little jute sacks and separate them. She had the memory of an elephant. She knew the name of every herb and what they were good for.

Juana la Callá is a walking pharmacy. That's what people would say about my grandma. She could list all the wild herbs in the area. If you were into spiritualism and herbs, the eastern part of Cuba, el Oriente, was a goldmine. But if she started, it would be a never-ending story. However, I do remember that for a cold, the best was a concoction made of rosemary with bee's honey and lemon. If your fever wouldn't go away, you'd get the bark of a cuaba tree—she'd make it for me—, take a hot bath with it and goodbye fever.

Ragweed parthenium could get rid of any sickness. Well, it at least worked for skin problems and hives. And there's nothing like chamomile for your stomach. Chamomile cures eighteen types of sicknesses. My ears would get filled with dirt and become infected at night. Sometimes it was painful. So my grandma would put drops of sorrelvine sap in my ears; it was very potent and very effective. There wasn't one single trace of medicine or eye-drops in my house. Herbs were peasants' medicine.

Palm trees and coconuts take care of mostly everything in the countryside. You need a palm tree for just about anything. Houses in the countryside are made of palm trees; a hut is basically a palm tree taken apart, right? Even cattle eat parts of palm trees. Coconuts, My gosh! They're used to bathe newborns. When I was born, they poured coconut water on my head and feet. It's also good for the kidneys, gonorrhea, and anemia. It can be used as a laxative, hair tonic, and much, much more.

In the countryside there are infinite ways to come up with a cure: sticks from the swampy tropical forest, seeds, roots, tree bark . . . "A *curandero* with no *jiba* root, can't cure anything," was a popular saying where I come from. *Jiba*, centaury, root would really cure everything. The folk medicine healers would say that if you went to cut it without praying for why you wanted it, you'd get it and it wouldn't work. First, you had to get close to it and whisper: "*Jiba* root, sacred stick, I want you to cure so-and-so of whatever," and then break off a whole piece. In my house, there was always a cross made of *jiba* stick and nutmeg for eye, mouth, and bone problems. It would get rid of anything: tuberculosis, parasites, syphilis, lung problems and even migraines, which are very common in the countryside because the sun is like fire and when it gets into your head, ice won't even get rid of it.

Then there were the sacred sticks, the ones the *espiritistas* used. Paradise was the big one because it was said to bring good luck. My mother was always praying to Anima Sola with paradise branches: "Paradise, paradise make my luck better so that it is just as good as you are long." But we always had bad luck. Paradise couldn't even help my family's fate. And it was the countryside. It was the fate of *guajiros*, working in the sugar fields, on land that was in a vulnerable situation, threatened by the mill owners and powerful *colonos*. We didn't have a lot to lose because we were poorer than a church mouse, but I saw many families flee from the rural guard when it was eviction time. There was a lot of talk about Realengo 18 and rightfully so, because that's where Lino Álvarez stopped the narrow path that Batista tried to make. Under the slogan "*Tierra o Muerte*," "Land or Death," he united men from the countryside to form a very solid front.

Something similar happened in San Felipe de Uñas. In 1932, the *Comités de Lucha*, the Struggle Committees, joined forces to go up against the government and the rich. They wanted to strangle the hardworking *guajiro*, the sugarcane cutter, the cart driver, the one who worked at the mill and transported and loaded sugar, the one who did all the hard work; in other words, the slave. In Cuba, the *guajiros* took all the abuse. At least if you lived in the city, you had other options, although you'd go through more jobs than cot covers. It was different, there was hope in the city. It offered change, adventures. The countryside was sadly the same thing over and over again, that's all it was.

The fighting records in the eastern part of the island made up some of the longest in Cuba. The Jobabo Sugar Mill in Virama was made up of hundreds of *caballerías*—each *caballería* was 33.6 acres of land—, but in other places everything was upside-down. They couldn't get anything together because the Comuneros Group was pretty powerful and opposed barbaric resistance. A child, like myself, couldn't face this reality. Mostly because the only thing I did was line up bundles of sugarcane. But I'd hear and realize what was going on. There were so many strikes and hunger strikes. It was nothing but hell.

Tomás would get to my house all stupid and think he was in

charge of everything. But he was nothing more than a poor *colono* with a lot of women in the area, and my mother would more or less pay attention to him so she could at least give us bread and milk. When I'd come home, I'd be in a bad mood and covered with dirt, and I'd find that big drone sipping coffee and playing Mr. Nice Guy singing *"Los feos pa' la cocina."* It was a popular song at the time. I'd feel like hitting him over the head with a hoe. I'd control myself though because a peasant holds his rage inside. They're not like city people who are loud mouths and let it all out and it ends up just being noise. I really wanted to get rid of that pig. But my family would lose everything and my sister was still little, although she'd cut wood and scrub my work pants and flour sack shirts clean.

Soon after I started in the sugarcane fields my brother Pascual became a cart driver. There was no more hanging from the branches of the plum trees and rolling in sheaths from the palm trees. Pascual was always more timid than I was, more reserved. He didn't talk. No one knew what he was thinking. My brother Pascual was a true natural *guajiro*. And then there was Yara. She was a happy child. She'd sing Mexican songs and put her hair in long braids every day and wait for her prince charming from the soap operas on the radio to come. She had her first boyfriend when she was thirteen and the damage she did to our family was a horse of a different color. That's why I'm going to continue with the story about my mother and Tomás Duarte.

It was Saint John's Day, June 24, right when they were burning the *muñeco*, the dummy, in the open area in our town. It was the only celebration that we'd go to. We'd celebrate Christmas Eve in the short cut between our shack and my maternal grandparents' place. It was a boring poor people's feast because there was no father and my grandmother didn't like parties. As I already said, my grandmother was a strange and domineering woman and the nickname Juana la Callá suited her well.

Just like the pig, you can't put lipstick on a rat. Tomás was cunning and greedy. I'll never forget it: there we were in the middle of the party, when I hear voices and someone screaming. It was that shameless Duarte trying to get my sister away from everyone and take her to the forest to devour her. Of course she screamed and he got caught. Like a real coward, he got out of there fast. My sister threw herself into my mother's arms. Pascual and I ran after him but we couldn't catch him because the bastard was a mountain *jutía*, a rodent. The entire village found out about what had happened. The evil-tongued people were saying that my mother would see him in secrecy, but it wasn't like that. I'm sure of it because if she loved anyone, it was my sister Yara. When we got home that day my sister was crying and my mother going from the fire to the patio with her usual: "Just shoot me! Just shoot me!"

If my family had sixty cents a day it was a lot. Life was a sea of pain in my town. Thank God my brother and I had work in the countryside. I learned to write when I got to Havana. Just like everyone else, I'd count with little balls or stones, depending on the situation. And I'd write my name by putting anything down or by copying it from other papers. "J" is an easy letter, and the "M" of my last name you can write with your eyes closed. But I took my first lessons in Havana when I was around people from the city, worldly people. They were more fickle than *guajiros*, but more complicated. *Guajiros* might daydream a lot, but they're noble at heart. It's because of the land.

I was an absentminded kid despite my hectic life. I'd stare up at the sky a lot. It's true what *guajiros* say about the clouds. If you stop and take a good look, you'll see they duplicate everything we have here on earth: ploughs, yoke, wagons, women laying down and women standing up, dogs, turkey vultures. Clouds form all these things when you have a sky scattered with white clouds.

I was a good listener. I knew all the stories that my family told as well as the ones from the sugar fields. Fantastic stories that the *guajiros* later sang in *décimas* and *puntos*. That's why I say that the philosophy of someone from the countryside is in the songs the *guajiros* sing. I'd hear over and over again the story about some guy's daughter, who'd gone off to the city in a fancy car with a man with a mustache and slicked-back hair, and dressed in white. Later, she'd be in the newspapers for some scandal at the brothels in the Colón neighborhood. That was more common than purslane, a weed in the area. That explains why my mother had my sister tied to a chain because Yara's eyes were very beautiful and they were always looking where they shouldn't be. And that's when every once in a while one of those bastards would come around and steal women from the hamlets. They'd promise them villas and castles, they'd take them away and then throw them in the gutter or put them in a whorehouse. The girls would be embarrassed and wouldn't want to go back to their families.

That's what happened to one of my cousins. She had beautiful black hair and olive skin. She was the pride of the entire *cuartón*. One day she took off and her mother said she'd gone to Havana to get over an illness. No one found out how she got out of there. Some said she disguised herself as an old lady and went on a cargo train. Others say someone put her on a horse and left her on the highway, where a truck took her to Holguín. Some would also say her stepfather traded her in exchange for some animals. There was always some skeleton in the closet. I do know for sure that my cousin Emelina Mesa Castillo got her hands dirty around the time of the assassination of Antonio Guiteras. In my town the people would not shut up about Guiteras's death and my cousin's picture in the newspaper *Carteles*. She was surrounded by young girls who just got to the city. Their eyes were wide-open and about to pop out of their head. When my sister talked about a potential suitor my mother would warn her, "Remember what happened to your cousin Emelina. That can't happen to you, Sweetie."

Yara was always a good homemaker but she didn't have any luck with her first boyfriend. It was nothing like what happened to Emelina, that's for sure, but I don't know if in the end it was worse because my sister was left, as they say, with nothing. After a few months of dating, her boyfriend deflowered her and then took off. She didn't say a thing about it. She knew that between my mother and my grandfather they'd kill her, but her stomach began to get bigger and bigger each day. I imagine that the poor girl must've felt a burning fire inside, because hiding it from the family until the seventh month of pregnancy must've been torture.

My grandmother discovered her. One afternoon Yara was hanging the clothes on the line. She wasn't paying much attention because she thought no one was watching her until my grandmother let out a scream that must've stopped her heart: "Yara! Yara! Please tell me I'm seeing things!"

Like a little dog, my sister hunched over and totally collapsed on the floor. I was still in the field, but my brother was home already. When I got there, I saw my sister crawling on the ground, with her eyes full of tears. And my grandparents were silent and serious. My grandmother froze and my mother kept saying: "Just shoot me! Just shoot me!" Pascual said to me, "Stay calm, Julián. This woman is going to either set herself on fire or drown herself. We're going to help her. Even if it's really painful, she's the only sister we've got."

Cayetano Andrés was born during the next sugarcane harvest. My grandmother gave my nephew his name. There was happiness with no party, but happiness afterall, because my sister was a saint and she had ram eyes and she was so pretty and so good that she deserved to be forgiven. Since I never had a son, I always felt both affection and shame towards Andrés. Then my sister met a man and went to live with him in Holguín. They had other kids, but I was especially fond of Andrés and if God didn't give you a son, the Devil gave you a nephew. I say that Andrés is kind of my son, too. Oh by the way, and this is off topic, but I'm proud of it: he's a machine engineer for a sugar mill called Urbano Noris, one of the largest, I believe.

The nightly entertainment was telling stories and lies. I was a mess by the time I got home because the sugarcane fields were far away, very far away, and I had to walk a lot to get there and back. My town was fertile land of inferior products and the sugarcane was a ways away and harvested for a mid-sized sugar mill. I've got a bank of stories and lies in my mind. We'd fall asleep to the stories told by relatives who'd go to visit my grandfather. Each one was more exaggerated than the last. Between the stories, the lies, and the tongue twisters, we were entertained for hours.

"I wish to wish the wish you wish to wish, but if you wish the wish the witch wishes, I won't wish the wish you wish to wish." Who could say that one really quickly? Nano, the mulatto; he knew all the stories and tongue twisters and was incredibly talented at saying them. One of Nano's tongue-twisters is: "One-one was a race horse. Two-two was one too. One-one won one race. Two-two won one too." It seems easy, but the trick is to say it three times in a row fast without messing up.

Here's one of his best stories. There's a little *guajiro* who doesn't want to try a sandwich, and his mother says to him, "Eustaquio, if you don't eat it, the devil's going to come and take you away." The boy looked at his mother with a perplexed look on his face and asked her, "Mommy, is the devil a man?" And the mother answered, "No son, worse." Then the son said to her, "Is it a woman then, Mommy?"

A little cat and a cow were on their way to a party. They were all dressed up and ready to go. The cow, as tormented as she is, tried to pick on the small and stubborn cat. The cow says, "Everyone look at him, teeny tiny with those whiskers." And the cat then got mad and said to her, "You're so big and don't even have a bra on."

Then there were the stories about the lazy *guajiro*, the town dummy, the witches, the priest and the rural guard. When it was late, Nano, tired of talking, would always bring up the one about the fool. He'd say: "Since, you guys aren't getting tired, I'll tell you the one about the dupe. There was a man who lived alone with his wife in a house in the countryside. One day they were waiting for the dupe to come over . . ." And we'd say to him: "Come on, Nano, tell us the one about the husband and wife." Then he'd say: "You have to wait until the dupe comes over" and he'd continue, "You have to wait until the dupe comes over, you have to wait until the dupe comes over: and by then we, fighting to keep our eyes open, would fall asleep.

Nano and my grandparents would bang their stools against the walls of the *bohío* when they had nothing left to do to make the night go by any faster; they'd start to remember things about this one and that one. That's how they came up with stories like the one about the *isleña* witch who'd go get dressed at Nano's house. She'd steal the first broom and black cloth she could find. Then she'd spread potash all over her armpits to get power from the air and start to fly, hissing. The witch would leave a yellow trail that looked like a light tail. Or the glow of a chorus of angels that came out one night from behind a bush and sang wonderfully until my grandmother tried to turn her head. When someone would try to see it, it'd immediately disappear behind the trees. My family would get scared and for weeks no one said a word about apparitions. Living in the countryside unleashes your imagination to the supernatural. That's why peasants are such liars when they start to make up their stories. You've got to do something to break the monotony. Roosters' crows and jealous *guajiros* fighting with machetes over what some woman had done just weren't enough.

Juvenal Cateura lived a stone's throw away from my house. He was a tall, olive-skinned *guajiro* with thick eyebrows and little facial hair. He had three daughters with Zoila la Bonita—she was really beautiful—and he lived in that *bohío* since Machado broke up with gunshots a hunger march against the employers. He played a major role in that turmoil and came out of it a brave and truthful man. Juvenal was a vegetable picker and my brother Pascual would help him move things around town and with planting. Ever since the thing with Tomás Duarte happened, Juvenal became our friend and every once in a while he'd send us bread and sweets, and some meat when he could. We were friends even though I'd hardly ever go there because Juvenal's daughters were always very dressed-up with flowers in their hair and starched skirts. And like I said before, I was a piece of dirt. Ever since I was a kid, I was a big show off and that's why I didn't like to be seen like that. It was only on Sundays that I'd dress up and go out so the people in my town could see me.

Zoila la Bonita had milky white skin, big eyes, and hair down to her waist. She looked like a little virgin. But *guajiro* men are very distant from their wives and once they're married and have children they think that they've got nothing to worry about. Juvenal really did a number on Zoila. They say he made her suffer a lot. Despite being a serious man, he liked a good cock and liquor. Between the cockfights and the alcohol, Juvenal destroyed it all in no time. When he'd come from town and Zoila would ask him for something, Juvenal would say, "You're always asking me for something, damn it! As if everything were free. Here!" And what he'd give her wouldn't even be enough to buy a ribbon for her hair. Their daughters, all very beautiful as well, were always in their Sunday best, very put together, but always in the same clothes. Juvenal was very stingy.

And even though there wasn't all that much to buy, every once in a while Amín the Arab would come by with his saddlebags filled with junk. A traveling salesman with a lot of imagination and cheap stuff was a big deal in those *cuartones*. People would say "The May showers are here" when they'd see him coming on his mare. He was a peaceful Arab and quiet as a tomb, but he did have a sly look on his face. People figured he was in love with one of Juvenal's daughters and that's why he was fluttering around there so much. No one could guess for sure which one was his favorite. There wasn't anyone who would have ever suspected that he was doing his thing with Zoila la Bonita. I've thought about it several times and I could never figure it out. I don't know if she was bored of Juvenal or if it's because the Arab gave her some money. I just don't know.

My mother was the one who told me the news. I was coming with a bucket of water and threw it down and quickly ran over there. Zoila's three daughters were gathered around her like three little chicks and the mother hen. They didn't stop screaming. Juvenal, half drunk, came through the back of the *bohío* and saw the Arab caressing Zoila's breasts. At least, that's what people said. He took out his machete and cut Amín's head right off. When I got there, the rural guard hadn't yet arrived and Amín's head was next to the logs and looked like a beat-up pineapple. Blood was flowing furiously and Zoila, holding her daughters tightly, screaming: "What on earth!"

Pascual put the Arab's head in a sack and was the one who explained everything to the rural guard. Zoila and her daughters, with their eyes bulging out of their heads, were silent and stayed right beside the fire. Juvenal, there's no need to say it, was never seen again. Later, some people said they saw him in Barnes as a sugarcane cutter and in Havana as a lottery ticket seller. There was a lot of gossip going around. There were so many different stories. To make a long story short, when someone butted in and asked the women in the area what happened, they'd always say the same thing, "The earth swallowed him."

My brother Pascual eventually became the boyfriend of one of the daughters of Zoila la Bonita and Juvenal. But my grandmother would tell him the same thing over and over again, "The family is cursed, My Son. Everything there smells of blood." Pascual didn't pay any attention to her because he fell in love with the middle girl. Her name was also Zoila and she was almost as pretty as her mother. That was one of the crudest stories about men fighting. That's what it was like in the countryside. That's why I wanted to get out of there.

When sugarcane is dry, walking on it is worse than walking on nails. Everything that has to do with sugarcane is brutal. But that's not how it is today, that's for sure. The modern machines, the gatherers and cutters, make the work a lot easier. But before you had to do it all by yourself. When you were in a desperate situation, you wanted to have another arm so you could cut more and earn a little more. My grandfather was always a vegetable picker. He got to have his own little piece of land, but he lost it when Menocal was in office. That's why we became so vulnerable. He'd have given anything so that I wouldn't have to go cut anymore. My personality was better suited to be a harvester. But they didn't earn a thing.

Sugarcane was my last job before leaving for Havana. Sometimes I'd help put a roof on a *bohío* by breaking up the branches of a palm tree, the *guano*, or getting leaves from the trestle. I liked to participate in this event, *la cojiba*, because all the neighbors and friends would get together and drink rum, and eat roasted pork cooked over an open fire and fried *jutía*. The owner of the house would provide the food and drink. Sometimes a *guajiro* would show up with his guitar and sing puntos and Mexican rancheras. They'd organize some big parties there, although sometimes blood would be shed. It's not that I only remember the bad things about living in the countryside, but a peasant's life was hardly ever peaceful. Too much abuse.

Nicknames caused a lot of trouble. Men from the countryside don't like to be called anything for short. If you dared to use one, you were putting your life on the line. Especially during the *cobija*, when the guys would get together to work. I saw this with my own eyes. And if it's a lie, I shall be cursed by Júa, that's the dummy we burn on Saint John's Day. Pascual, my grandfather, and I were helping to put a roof on Bertino Mola's house. I was breaking up *guano* when I hear Bertino saying to someone, "Marcial, leave that man alone. Don't say anything to him."

The man was a rural guard officer, that's all. He was coming on horseback to drink rum and eat a slice of pork or perhaps to see what was up. But he was a very conceited and abusive police officer. He was known to be a pimp. He'd look lustfully in the *cuartones* . . . A leech! He jumped over the Mormon tea plant and there he was, at arm's length. He asked for rum and we gave it to him. He asked for a *jutía* sandwich, and we gave it to him. But he didn't even offer to help out.

The Cristinillas sisters were his victims. The pervert had stolen some animals from them and even some towels that they had hanging out on the line. Everyone knew about it. No one liked him. People watched out for him. They started to call him "Chicken Snatcher," but no one dared to say it to his face because he was scum and he'd walk around armed up to his neck. When he got on his horse to leave, Marcial shouted at him, "Chicken Snatcher, shame on you!" To make a long story short, he took out his gun and shot Bertino twice in the forehead. We were stunned, and went after him while he took off on his horse. That crime remained unpunished. He was given another position, in another province. I don't know. But we didn't even go to Bertino's wake. We spent two days and two nights looking for him. We even looked in ferret holes. There wasn't any justice in the countryside until today. I'm sure of it because of what they've told me and from what I've read.

In my dreams about the countryside, I keep seeing the same thing: the Cristinillas sister with their heads wrapped in big towels, in the sun's glare, going to get my sister Yara to pray. How's it possible that I still have that image in my head? New York is something else but it still comes back every once in a while like a movie. I guess memory must be part of our imagination. Despite time and distance, certain things stick with us although they might be distorted. My godfather, the way he'd look at you, his demeanor, even his voice, are things that are still with me. He was what's called in Cuba a "*jabao* mulatto" because of their light skin, blue eyes and light, wooly hair. They usually come from the area north of Oriente which has a mix of races, and the North Americans also left a drop of their blood there.

Many times people ask me why I complain about having worked so much if that was a rich area, with sugar mills and Yankee properties with bungalows and all of that. And I say that was what it was like in the *bateyes* and close to the mines like in Nicaro and Moa. But where I lived was cursed. It was a lost land, a flat and very vulnerable area. To tell the truth, the poorest part of Oriente, where misery was something very serious, was the south, the black strip of Manzanillo, Pilón, Guantánamo, and Baracoa. And, of course, the Sierra Maestra. In some of those little towns on the coast, the cemeteries were close to the cliff, close to the sea or in the sea itself. In my town, we at least had a small cemetery where there had once been a field. However, to go to school you had to walk so much that once you got there you were completely beat. My godfather Julián would come give us a ride from Pascuas to San Juan and he wanted me to study. "Oxen exist, and they learn to plow, why don't you go and learn to read?" But I was reluctant to study back then, I wanted money so I could do what I wanted to.

Julián would send a crew of hardcore Haitian cutters. They were lions in the sugarcane fields. They'd take potions to work and they'd become possessed by a zombie. The zombie would work for them. They'd talk to them, they'd crush sugarcane on the ground so they'd drink it. Something strange was going on there, because you'd see them go in the sugarcane fields and then come out as fresh as lettuce. My godfather preferred Haitians to do the cutting. Since they were in the area, he'd take advantage of them when forming his crews. The Haitians would put together their Gagá parties with flags, stave drums, and lucid dances. They'd carry a table in their mouths, pass a machete to each other with their mouths, there was no limit to what they could do.

They'd tell Julián that Cubans also had their own zombies. It was because Cubans, used to being in the sugarcane field, cut like someone who was possessed and there were times when not even the Haitians could follow their lead. The zombie was a spirit that went in the body of an old Haitian or a *pichón*, that's what they called their descendents born in Cuba. The Haitian crews were strong with or without the zombie. And on occasion they stirred feelings of suspicion in the sugar mill, they created friction, because they had very low salaries and they took jobs away from the natives. My godfather exploited them quite a bit. That's why he threw in his hen and managed to help me out with what I wanted to do: get out of there.

Although I left when I was sixteen, life in the countryside had everything. I saw a lot, I was very observant. As a child, I was a dope. I was very absentminded and shy. I'm proud to say that my first sexual experiences were wild, as it should be in the countryside.

I'm not ashamed of it. A few months before leaving, I went to Virama, close to Victoria de las Tunas, with some friends. I met a prostitute in a shed for the practice of her profession. In the front part they sold beer and cigarettes and the women wearing loud colors and bold flowers in their hair were in the back. They all looked the same to me, except for one. She called me over right away and I went and told her, "I'm here just to look. That's all."

"No one comes here for that and I don't want little boy stories."

When I was going, she called me over again and whispered in my ear, "Do you know what your friends are going to say about you?"

"No."

"That you're a fag . . . Do you have any money?"

"Yes," I told her.

"Go, go buy a beer and bring it," she said to me, undoing the bra underneath her dress.

I bought the beer and I went with her to a little room where there was an iron bed and a stained mirror.

"If you continue to wear that hat your hair's going to fall out," she told me softly. She got undressed right away. She didn't waste any time. But that didn't do it for me. It was my first time.

Before that it was with Genaro's baby goat. It's true. There were these baby goats called "the Pure Ones" because that's what they were for. The boys would wash them with perfumed soap and smother them with cheap perfume. But this time it was a woman and she was pretty, very pretty. That night, the heat was suffocating and I was sweating seas. I thought about the worst things. A chatty Haitian, one of my grandmother's friends, would always say prostitutes didn't have bellybuttons because they were daughters of the devil. I looked at her stomach, and I don't know if it was an optical illusion or if it was for real, but I didn't see her bellybutton. Her skin was as smooth as a rubber ball. When she went to hug me, I shunned her and said, "Take this."

I tossed two pesos on the bed for her, that was all I had, and I got out of there in a flash. The next day my friends asked me, "Did you go out with a bang, Julián? We waited for you outside and you didn't come out. You're a jerk, damn it. He's a wolf in sheep's clothing."

"When the ox finds a spot, he opens his ass so that flies go in," I answered, forcing myself to laugh.

I have never been able to forget that night. In my life I've been with very attractive women, but I never again slept with a prostitute. I met them, I knew them in Havana, I see them on a daily basis in this city where they gather on the East Side, but I never wanted to repeat an experience like that. For me, sex is the lubricant of life and it should be done willingly and without any pressure. Wouldn't you agree?

"What's up, Brother? You're acting strange. Is something wrong?"

Yara was very serious, very mature. She could tell that I wanted to get out of there.

"Nothing's wrong, Sister, but there's nothing for me to look forward to."

That poor little thing didn't have an answer for me. She would look me over like someone whose heart aches but doesn't know why. My last weeks at home were spent working the sugar boilers. At least it was no longer an entire day from sun up to sun down and out in the open. I'd look at my 15-year-old brother and think he was built like a little cargo donkey. Yara had her head in the clouds, not thinking about anything; those years would leave anyone stupefied. My mother was still collecting wood, cooking and cleaning with the roof collapsing over her head. Our *bohío* looked a little better on the outside, but inside it was still a coffin with windows.

The countryside was very sad, very desolate for someone like me. I needed some adventure! I was tired of getting up when it was still dark and going to bed shortly after the sun goes down. I was fed up with the rain that gets to your bones, the droughts, the rooster's crow, I don't know . . . Now it's all so beautiful in my memory, because it is beautiful, it is healthy and gives meaning to life, but in those years it was bitter to me, it was torture. I know I did like the train's whistle. I'd hear it in the distance and it would startle me. That's when I got the idea to go to the capital.

"Look, I want to go work in Havana."

"You don't have to stay here," my godfather said.

His words were like putting twenty pesos in my hand.

"Tell your grandparents and your mother that you're going to do a job for me."

When I had everything ready, when the only thing left do to was to tell my grandparents and my mother—I mention them because for Yara and Pascual it was no secret that I was making a move—the most impressive fire I've ever seen broke out. The fire almost came within an inch of my house. All the sugarcane turned to ash. The animals were running all over the place. It was as if Satan had done it. I went to lend a hand.

We opened a clearing with machetes to put it out with another fire, but the flames slashed like sabers. The only way to put out the fire is to start another one. You only know that if you've lived in the countryside. You quickly open a clearing by cutting the sugarcane down really low. Then you take the stalks away and let some of the flames push the others.

People die in that kind of battle. I've seen them die because of thick smoke suffocation and because their bellies caught on fire. My own father was burned to death. There's no way to control the flames when they say "we're here." That's another thing about the countryside: violent things happen in the middle of peaceful-ness. Someone would die and no one would care. The only thing that would happen would be a funeral and some crying. I also saw many women die of suffocation in the sugarcane fields in Oriente.

I almost didn't say goodbye to anyone. I felt bad about it because there were people I had to thank for friendship or work. I thought, "Now, I'm going to be alone, but what does it matter? Dogs can roam around by themselves and survive, right?"

If I think back, I picture a green, very green, sown field with lots of sugar shoots, the sugar mill's smokestack, and the path, with the morning glories running along it, leading to our *bohío* and to my grandmother's. I feel the hot rain of the sun's glare and the humidity of the countryside that gets in your bones. It was raining a lot that day and because I was constantly thinking about everything, when my mother woke me up for work, the first thing I said to her was "I'm going to Havana."

"What are you talking about, Julián? Were you dreaming?"

"No, I wasn't dreaming. I'm going to Havana."

"Yara! Pascual! Come here! Your brother's gone crazy!"

"I'm leaving for Havana right now."

"Oh, Holy Mother, more pain!"

She wasn't a bad mother although she did love the *fogón* more than her children. She fed us but her affection always seemed to me to be . . . She was irritated about something that day. But I put on a blindfold and plugged my ears. My sister and brother didn't say a word. Yara smiled at me and Pascual put on a tough face in order to hide his feelings. However, my mother got extremely sad. She sat on a stool, lowered her head and even forgot to strain the coffee. I put on my best clothes, a white cotton shirt and pants from the store. Pascual went and told my grandparents what was going on. My grandmother, Juana, hugged me before anyone else did. She put a black string around my neck and told me in a shaky voice, "May your guardian angel protect you." My grandfather looked at me coldly in the eyes and wished me luck, "Send a telegram when you get there. That's what people do."

Carolina, my grandmother's Haitian friend, got there when I was almost all ready to leave. I saw her coming up the path. She got me a little scared because people called her "A bad luck bird" along with a million other things. However, she always behaved like part of the family. "I hope everything works out for you," she said to me.

I looked at her thinking about all the sugarcane she'd cut in her life and gave her a hug. Some of the boys from the hamlet showed up with towels on their heads and although the rain had eased up, they got there soaking wet to say goodbye or just because they were curious. My brother went to tell everyone and almost the entire town gathered in front of the door to my house. When it seems as though my mother couldn't manage any longer to control herself, she hugged me crying. I promised to send her money and when I really learned to write, to write her some letters so my grandfather could read them to her. The boys crowded around the door of the *bohío* and out of curiosity they said things to each other. My mother scared them away by clapping her hands and they scurried away on the path like frightened little mice. My grandmother brought coffee and we had a little in silence. My godfather Julián was the only one I left a message for. He deserved it, I always thought.

It was drizzling when I started my journey. I didn't look back. Yara was the one who walked next to me the longest. Then I asked her to go back home. I promised her villas and castles and although I would've liked to do such a thing, I always knew I wasn't going to be able to. But just like dreaming doesn't cost a thing . . . , promises don't either.

I walked through the milky mud, avoiding the furrows fattened by the rain, knowing that I'd only return to my house to visit. I sweated a lot because the sun was shining directly down on me. A hot sun, a rain sun. In Cuba, when it rains like this, with that little sun burning, they say that the devil's getting married. I never found out what that means exactly. People's wisdom is more mysterious than that of the wise, I say. When I got to a place called Vieja Gorda, close to the railroad track, I told my sister to go back home. She'd never given me a kiss. I begged her, "Go, Yara!" Old Alonso, the owner of the town bodega and a buddy of my godfather Julián screamed out "boy" to me about three times, and when I finally had him in my face, he softly whispered, "So you're going to live it up, you bastard."

Yara, with tears in her eyes, told me these words that I'll never forget, "Good gracious, Brother, you're leaving when the devil's getting married. Take care of yourself."

The Journey

Journeys are the offspring of feet.

There was absolutely nothing between the clearing and the train besides vultures devouring carrion. Morning hadn't broken just yet. I was a little cold waiting there for the train. The train that would take me to Santa Clara was made of wood. It was an old, dilapidated train, but it had a whistle that you could hear from thirty miles away. The people from my village could tell what was going on just by that train's whistle. If so-and-so in some other hamlet was hanging himself, they knew it because of the whistle before or after it sounded. The whistle was always how they knew what was going on. It would go by between 10 and 10:30 every day so it was like the mid-morning rooster. For a man of the countryside that was an important hour, an hour of intense labor before the mid-day break. The train's whistle made me think about what I was about to do. I said to myself, "Why are you going to pay for the ticket if you can hop on the last car, the one with all the mail in it? Hide yourself real good between the sacks, pretend you're one of them, and off we go!"

I kept the little money I had because I wanted to make it on my own. I was going to face the world. That's how it was, right? I had to make it count being that I didn't have anything else. I thought of a thousand things. Some of my relatives went to Havana to look for work and in a blink of an eye they were swindled and had to come up with the money to get back home. I remembered what happened to my cousin Emelina Mesa Castillo. She got her hands dirty when Guiteras was killed. I remembered when Eleuterio Vega's son, the poor thing, stayed for two days at the Isla de Cuba Hotel and his money was stolen out of the pocket of his *guayabera*. He begged for alms at the churches. And when he pretty much got back on his feet, he rented a room in a all-male boarding house and for years he'd sleep with his shoes on so that no one would steal his money.

When I was thinking about all those characters and crouching down so the conductors wouldn't see me, the train finally pulled in. It made its regular stop at the crossroads and a couple with two children got on. When the train was going to pull away, I forced open the mail wagon's door, threw the sack to the back and dove into the pile. With the clatter of the wagon and the whistle blasting in my ears, I tried to get comfortable between the boxes and packages. And after a few seconds, almost without even noticing, the train was moving.

It was my first time on a train. I liked seeing the electric posts and the trees disappear in a fraction of a second. The sensation of leaving something behind, separating yourself from the place where you've always lived is both happy and sad. On the one hand, you abandon it all to throw yourself into the world; on the other, there's the unknown, a muted rooster. I believed I was going to conquer Havana. I would take a bite out of the earth, as they say.

During the ride the train stopped about one hundred times. Every time really scared me on that adventure. I filled my pockets with *rompequijadas*. I bought a pound of bread and a can of condensed milk and thought: "This'll keep my stomach happy until I get to the capital." Who was I fooling?! After eight or ten hours on the road, hunger said "I'm here." I became antsy.

I got off at a weigh station in the province of Las Villas. I remember it so clearly. I bought a sandwich and used the restroom. When I got back to the car, I found the door wide open. I'd left it only halfway opened. I tried to go to a passenger car but someone grabbed my arms, and without even asking me my name, they took me to the rural guard headquarters: a pigsty with a bunch of guys in t-shirts playing dominoes. I wanted my suitcase, my clothing, the stuff I had with me, but the lieutenant didn't let me say a word. I'd go to say something and he'd give me the look of death. "You're up to something, you're up to something," he'd say to me. And then he decided to ask me what I was doing.

"I'm going to look for a job in Havana," I answered.

"Tell that to someone else. You're in some political mess. You stole. You're a thief. It's written all over your face."

I looked hungry and scared, but not like a thief. No way! I showed him my hands. They had calluses all over them. They were leather. The hands of a mature man.

"I'm a sugarcane cutter," I told him.

"You're a rogue," he responded. "Get out of here!"

I was cleaning that slum for about six or seven days so I could eat. They made me do *guardia vieja*, which means I had to clean the outhouse and the stable. I dictated a letter to my godfather asking him for help, but I have no idea if he ever got it. When they let me go, they warned me, "Don't ever come back here alive."

To avoid a beating, I got out of there so fast that I didn't even make up my mind where I was going. After a few hours of feeling my way around Hatuey, that's what the place was called, I met some men who were going to a weigh station to look for work cutting sugarcane. I could tell immediately that they were humble people, a little ragged, but hardworking. When I told them about my bad spell, they said: "Come with us." They were headed towards the Washington Sugar Company to look for work. Although it seems like a tall tale, one of them, a well-built, young, strong, black man was walking around with only one shoe on. And it was old.

"Why do you only have one shoe on?" I asked.

"Because I don't have any others," he answered.

They were poor people who didn't have much luck on their side. And to top it off, they were communists from what I heard them say. At that time, saying you were a communist was like saying you were the Devil himself. But I pretended I didn't realize. I was interested in finding work so that I could make some money and keep moving towards Havana with a ticket I'd paid for.

They called the black man Matanzas. He was bigger than a two-story house. He'd go around with another guy whose last name was Plaza, but they called him Placita. Communists would give each other nicknames to cover up their real names because things were really bad for them back then. We got to the weigh station and they told us flat out: "We have no work."

That was a slap in the face. I told them I was leaving even if I had to walk. But they persuaded me, "Stay, Julián." I stayed.

I was spent.

Placita and Matanzas lived in a barracoon next to the hamlet. To get there we walked, guided by the light of the full moon, along a wide, muddy path through the sugarcane fields. It was endless. The barracoon was a stick in a rectangular piece of land. It had one window and was only big enough for two people. That's when I heard them talk about the situation, the lack of work, and about someone named Manolito Andares. Manolito made black lists and went after communists in all the sugar mills in the area. With that hazard no one would hire them and they knew it.

That's why they advised me to stuff my face as fast as I could. They made a big soup with bones from the butcher shop's garbage cans and a little something else. They made a toast to me. I ate it as if it were a hearty stew. I was starving and that filled my stomach and reignited my desire to continue my journey. There was no way to get ahead with them because the poor things were worse off than I was. They didn't even have hope that something would work out for them in Havana. But, I didn't give up. I could've stayed there some days, in that barracoon, listening to the most incredible stories in the world, but I closed my eyes and said to myself: "Julián, don't get in any deeper." But it's one thing to tell yourself how it's going to be and another thing is what life gives you.

My plan was to get to Havana with the desire to take on the world. I went to a nearby river and dunked my head in the water. Since it was hot, I took off my clothes and went in all the way for a good while. I came up with thousands of ideas while I was swimming in that river. I first thought about stealing mangos and then selling them on the highway. But there was a lot of competition. The highway was full of people selling fruit. You'd sell something, but it wouldn't be enough to get by. I was already sixteen, and that was something to take into consideration. I wasn't a boy anymore, and the young, little *guajiros* were the ones who got all the attention with their straw hats, making palm leaves filled with mangos for a few pennies.

I thought about making a shoeshine box and heading towards Havana. I found brushes, scraps of flannel, cans of shoe polish, and even tubes of stain. With my hands full I said goodbye to the few people I knew there, at least the ones with whom I'd shared some bone soup. And I set out for the *bateyes*. Between the suitcase and the shoeshine box I looked like a pack mule. Since no one from those places knew me, I didn't care if one day I slept in the doorway of some house and the next under a couple pieces of wood.

The money from my godfather wouldn't even last me three days in the capital. I'd touch my pockets and the money wasn't burning yet. One day there was a beautiful rainbow beyond a hill and I thought about my grandmother. She told me that if you urinated on one of the ends of it, money would fall from the sky on you. Like a dumb ass, I started to walk just in case. I walked without reaching the end. I was dead so I leaned up against a tree and slept like a dormouse. When I woke up there was no trace of the rainbow left. Not even its shadow. I was lucky I still had my shoeshine box and suitcase to comfort me. Oh, the things you do when you're young! When I think about it all, it really makes me laugh.

A shoeshine boy is like a barber; they're both sponges. People tend to tell you everything about themselves and the talk of the town. That's how I found out about a lot of things: private matters that were sometimes irrelevant and also things people would do in order to get by. When I look back, I think about all the people who in five minutes told me their life story and then some: their wife had cheated on them, they had a child with Down's syndrome, or they had to steal so they could eat. Then I see the Americans here in New York who keep to themselves. I say to myself: "Cubans, there's nothing like them!" They're so honest and earnest.

I'm not a nationalist, but it infuriates me how people live in this country. If there's a wounded person on the street, no one touches them until the police arrive. I've seen human bodies bleeding in the middle of Fifth Avenue and people say: "How sad! Oh, how sad!" and don't even move an inch to do something about it. That's the way it is. You just got to accept it. If not, you'll torture yourself.

I was tired of sleeping in parks and under bridges so I looked for some scraps of wood and made myself a little shed so I could have a roof over my head for the time being. Camajuaní grew on me. I lived there for about two or three months, shining shoes and running errands for the village tycoon. He owned a car service. I'd go get milk for him from the tit of the cow on a farm almost forty miles away. I'd keep an eye on his house and wash his cars. He had some Fords with canvas tops, running boards and hand-crank starters. I put my shoeshine box in the door and a stand up to sell coconut candy and other sweets. I did make enough money for the trip to Havana, but the relationships I made there were worth more to me. I tried to stay for a few months.

Old Horacio was fat and stubborn. They called him "Trucutú," after the American comic strip *Alley Oop* from the early 30s, because he didn't care about anything. He stood in the door of the house eating bread and goat, and rubbing his belly so that everyone could see him. Since he had money, people would say to him, "How's it going, Horacio?" He'd answer with that deep voice of his, "Good people, damn it!" Then, I'd hear him very clearly, grumble under his breath: "Lazy, envious pieces of shit." If he had to step on someone's toes, he'd do it. He didn't respect anyone. If he could exploit someone, he did it. Little by little he owned the whole town. He even bought a traveling circus from Servando Picayo, a circus performer from Asturias who went around from place to place with a few scrawny animals and a big top full of holes. He said to him: "Look, you *gallego*, I'll buy this shit from you so the monkeys and dogs don't die of hunger. Don't think that I'm doing it for any other reason."

The *gallego*, that's what all Spaniards in Cuba were called, said: "Come on, you know it's worth something."

The circus really changed my life. It made me forgot about Havana for a little bit. It didn't appeal to me very much to be a blockhead; in fact, I was better off shining shoes. That's when I really faced the world on my own for the first time, living with other people. It's hell when poverty is all around!

Horacio brought the circus to life. He wanted everything painted. He patched the big top so it would keep out the rain. He fattened up the animals. He spent his money to get the circus going. But for him it was a one-way street, it was all for him, and no one's salary went up. I was the only new person in the company because I was inexperienced and wanted to work. He made his son administrator and with him as the foreman, we went almost all over Las Villas. Nicolás wasn't like his father. He was a nitwit with a tie on. He was hooked on playing the lottery and would lose like a crazy person. Afterwards he'd show up saying, "I have a liver stone" and he'd throw himself down on the bedspread to sleep it off. He lost everything gambling and drinking.

Circus life is very hectic and it trains you to do thousands of things. I developed biceps that you don't even see in Gold's Gym from carrying boxes and trunks. My legs were rockhard from all the walking from place to place, from one scrubland to the next. We'd find a place for the circus and I'd nail down the studs to the big top and put up the trapeze and the grandstand. I was also in charge of the props: some scraps of junk that were very dangerous for the acrobats. When everything more or less was in its place, I'd hang two pieces of wood held together by straps over my shoulders and advertise the event. I'd go around as man sandwich to the villages and hamlets. When I'd get back I'd give food and water to the animals. Nicolás was good for nothing. He didn't give a damn about his father's business. He'd wash down the day's earnings with liquor. Most of the time I'd be panting by the time I'd get back—in that heat and with that thing hanging on you for an entire afternoon was unbearable—and Nicolás had already given free passes to three or four boys just because they brought water to the animals.

Having the circus in a small village like that was like getting a new toy. During those years, it was the only entertainment in the countryside. Children didn't go to cock fights, and women didn't like seeing blood. Well, they also weren't allowed in. After a few weeks on the road, Nicolás paralyzed a part of his body and we carried him in a cart to Camajuaní. We stayed for some time in El Santo, a *batey* close to Encrucijada. Between Germán the clown and myself, we were in charge of keeping things going so it didn't go under.

We'd put on two shows daily. The price of admission was ten cents. Women were free. And there was an audience of about one hundred for each seating. Germán only had one suit with lining in different colors. I helped him change for each act. The first time I went in the ring was to help him with the balls and the dogs. I learned to train the animals. I got along better with them than with the cast of the show. Germán was the only generous person who wanted to help me out. He was the main attraction of the circus. He was still young and he'd sing and dance. The little kids would go crazy with joy when they saw Germán clowning around. I'd always think about Germán when I'd see other clowns in big, fancy circuses, but I never saw anyone as funny as Germán Pírez in any of them.

He enjoyed the circus; it was his life. Everything, even the smallest things, he'd take to heart. Right when he'd get up in the morning he'd start to rub his hands with sawdust. He was always the first one ready. He'd put on his makeup at eleven in the morning. He'd eat lunch with it on, play cards with it on. The circus meant everything to him. If there were only four people in the stands, he'd work with just as much enthusiasm as if they were filled. When Nicolás came back to the company as the big boss, Germán sat him down and said, "That boy there does as much work as three. I'd like to talk to your father."

They increased my salary to fifteen pesos per month. During the Miguel Mariano Gómez administration, that wasn't bad money for a kid like myself. But I wanted to be more. I wanted adventure. Germán also taught me how to dance and how to follow the rhythm of the band. Well, you couldn't really call it a band, it was a couple of saucepans and a drum. I'd dance while he'd change his hat and get the dogs out of the ring. And I even sang some French-style numbers. Some of those ballads like "*Cara sucia*," dirty face. You know, the type of songs to entertain kids. And they'd touch their cheeks and then look at their fingers. Germán and Toribio, another clown who was as old as La Cabaña, would do tricks with their hands, dance jotas with tambourines and tell stories to the little ones. When there was money in the box, we'd buy candies and pass them out to the people in the stands and folding chairs.

The little circus picked up a bit in the area around Cienfuegos, and so Horacio bought some little horse rides and a cotton candy machine. That really made Nicolás's belly big. We rushed him to the nearest hospital. Within a few days he died of cirrhosis. His liver failed. But the show went on. Then Horacio put one of his partners in charge.

The circus set up in Cienfuegos, complete with a carousel, a cotton candy machine, and stands that sold *empanadillas*, pork sandwiches, and beer. Women from the countryside would bring containers filled with milk punch and sell it to the crowd. The circus really made a ruckus there. Horacio's friend, Felipe Luna, knew what he was doing. He'd always been in the circus business and he could do it all: walk the tightrope better than anyone, the double trapeze act, eat fire, lie down on a bed of nails, and he could even do forward rolls very gracefully for someone his age. But he had a flaw: he trusted no one. When someone got on his bad side, he was all over them. He insulted them left and right by saying things like: "Son of a bitch, asshole or *rojo!*" He really liked *rojo*, red, because in the Spanish Civil War, Franco was getting rid of the communists and Barcelona had just fallen.

He could be a real bastard. He had the *tenia saginata* wiggling inside of him. He was more bitter than an old maid. Going from Nicolás to Felipe Luna was bad luck after a catastrophe. One night he showed up in the big top with two very attractive chicks. The white one was Rosalía and the mulatta was Palmira. Felipe said they were cousins. People like me from the countryside, used to crude sex, would go gaga over women like them. I never thought I could fall in love like I did. Since I was always worried about having enough money to eat, women hadn't entered my life just yet. That's why I went crazy about Palmira. She changed my mind about things. She awakened my childhood ideas about the circus and a globetrotter's life. It was love at first sight. Germán saw it coming and he warned me, "Luna is selfish. Young girls and whores aren't enough for him. He wants both cousins at the same time."

Palmira would play the maracas and dance to the drums. It's called the *rumba de cajón*. Rosalía would sing and dance a little too. The two of them livened up the atmosphere. Horacio gave them free food and clothing. Their goal was to make it to Havana. Palmira dreamed of working for an all-female group in the *aires libres*, the open-air café's, in the Prado and Rosalía would do anything that involved nightlife. Since the film *El romance de palmar* was the big thing, the two of them dreamed of being artists. Once you get that bug, there's no way to get rid of it. Palmira had made up her mind, Rosalía not so much. She'd follow whatever her cousin did. But they supported each other because they'd grown up together.

Since I was already eighteen at the time, I had that itch all throughout my body. When I'd walk by her, I'd get goose bumps.

I'd stare at her, undress her with my eyes. Then I'd lie face down on the cot because I was embarrassed that my fellow workers would notice my you-know-what. The more I wanted it to go away, the harder it got. I wanted that woman. If they'd offered me a position as Senator in the Capitol Building, I wouldn't have taken it. I only had eyes for Palmira's mouth, her skin. And what legs! She'd dance, I'd drool.

But Felipe Luna was a glutton. One girl wasn't enough for him; he wanted both. That's when my bad luck started. I didn't get intimidated though. I really wanted her, and I was willing to do anything for her . . . because what's bound to happen to you is going to get you no matter what.

One afternoon I drank four beers and went to look for her in a Cruces bar where she worked at night on the weekends.

"What are you doing here, boy?"

"I came to see you."

"If Felipe catches you here, he'll kick you out of the circus."

"Oh no he won't because you're not going to tell him a thing."

"I'm not, but the others . . ."

"You have the same eyes as my sister Yara," I told her.

She looked at me like she wanted me. Well, I was young and Felipe was an old eyesore.

"Wait for me around the corner, Julián."

I waited for her under a zinc roof on Banderas Street for about an hour. Finally she appeared with her hair all wet, and nervous because she was scared that Luna was watching her.

"Where are you taking me?"

"I don't know, let's go over there."

"I wasn't conceived in the scrubland, just so you know."

She went into the thicket with me. The forests around the sugarcane fields are damp and peaceful. There wasn't a soul in sight. I didn't believe my eyes. I pulled her against me and kissed her all over while taking off her clothes. Her skin was firm and smooth. Although in the darkness you couldn't see anything. Like a pro, I caressed her from head to toe. I couldn't do anything else.

I must've been kissing her for a while because I remember she suddenly said to me, "Julián, if you don't take your clothes off, this won't work."

I was stupefied. I didn't want to separate myself from her. I continued caressing her and telling her foolish things until she started to take off my shirt and everything else. We finally threw ourselves on the path. We frolicked there for hours almost without even realizing it. We were both really young. She was three or four years older than I was, but her skin was tight and glowing. She looked younger. There was no doubt that we both liked each other. I had never done it like that before, with a completely naked woman. I think I behaved. When you like someone, there's nothing to it, that's why Palmira and I got along wonderfully. At about three in the morning when we were leaving, she told me to let her go alone to town so it didn't look suspicious. We walked together on some paths and when we got closer to the village and I realized I had to let her go, I went crazy and grabbed her by the neck and started to kiss her. She pushed me away and started to walk alone. I was speechless. I stood watching her. I would have run to catch up with her, but I talked myself out of it and caught the bus to Cienfuegos. Everything was illuminated on the ride back. I was wide-awake. My head was spinning.

Palmira lived with her cousin in a shed next to the train station. Luna took care of the bills, of course. People made all kind of remarks, but he didn't care. He was a jerk and an exploiter. I wanted to turn Palmira's life around and take her to Havana with me. I kept promising her we'd go, but she didn't believe me. "Vain promises," she'd say to me, "you don't even have your own place, Julián." I worked like a dog after that. The energy came from within. It was because I had a woman. I think she fell in love with me. She'd do whatever I'd say. Germán was the only one who knew what was going on between us. He gave good advice. He kept saying to me, "Enjoy it, you kids. Just enjoy it." How did Palmira manage for Rosalía not to find out about us? I never asked. When women decide not to talk about something, they bury it deep down inside of them. I gave her a lot of sex and built her castles in the sky. I even said to her, "I have relatives in the capital so when it comes to housing, we're going to be comfortable."

"You're lying!"

We'd see each other every day of course, but we almost never said a word to each other. I'd go see her in Cruces on Saturdays and Sundays and with my little savings, I'd take her to Ventura Inn on the road to the highway. The circus work didn't weigh me down because I was as light as a feather. I did, however, worry about the circumstances. You do a lot of crazy things when you're young, that's for sure. And I was blind. I didn't even pay attention to what old Germán told me. Every night I promised Palmira, "I'll get you out of here."

"Oh, Julián!"

But I didn't have enough money to do it. I figured out that once we got to Havana, I should rent a room in a boarding house for the two of us until I got a job. The period of government provisions controlled Cuba and the economy was rock bottom. You could try to get ahead, but it was quite risky. The circus wasn't doing bad. Horacio had money to keep it going; it was his hobby. But with that monster Felipe Luna and my falling in love with Palmira, you couldn't mess around. It was a fight until the end. They say something in Cuba that when the sheath of the royal palm tree protects you, there isn't an *isleño* who'll take it away. It's true. But this time the sheath fell on my head. I made a big mistake. I'm going to tell you about it—perhaps it'll be a lesson for young people.

I started to watch Felipe. Every night he'd pick up the earnings and keep them in a round cracker can. He kept the can in an old wooden trunk. I watched him closely. When Palmira would ask me about our escape, I'd tell her, "Tomorrow, My Love. We're leaving tomorrow."

"Oh, Julián!"

Germán warned me several times, but I didn't pay attention. He knew something was up. A clown and a fortuneteller have more in common than two royal palm trees. Every night I'd follow Luna to his shed and come back in deep thought. And he realized what was going on.

"Not that, Julián. You're not that kind of person."

But Palmira was like a broken record, "Let's get out of here, let's get out of here." That was ringing in my ears. So here's what happened: I took advantage of Felipe's deep sleep and acted on the sly. I waited until dawn because during the day he'd always be around doing something: the books, chewing out an employee, or taking advantage of some woman. But at night he'd almost always sleep alone.

I took off my boots and like a cat I jumped out the only window in the shed. I did it all on my own. Palmira didn't even suspect I was up to something. Felipe had an enormous belly; it'd hang off the bed. If he got stabbed, his gut would have to be taken away in a wheelbarrow. There was nothing left of the Felipe who'd frolic around, the agile Felipe we once knew.

I almost fell on top of him, but he didn't feel a thing. I was like a cat, and he was in a deep sleep. I stood completely still for a minute, deciding whether or not to cover his mouth and tie up his arms if he started to breathe heavily. I wouldn't have been capable of harming a human being. I just wanted the money and to get out of there as fast as possible. I searched in the dark, opened the trunk, sniffed under the bed, then around the headboard, everywhere: the only thing I didn't do was search the pockets of his pants. And I couldn't because the beast slept with them on. Now, the problem was how to get out of there without making a peep.

I put one foot on the edge of the bed, the other on the headboard, and with my hands on the windowsill I hoisted myself up so that I'd fall over to the other side. As luck would have it, Felipe moved and my hairs stood on end. I froze; I was a statue. My jaw was locked shut. I couldn't move my feet. I felt a big charge throughout by entire body and a knot in my stomach. Without even making a sound in all that darkness, Felipe stood up and hit me good and hard. He didn't even realize who he was beating up. I tried again to get out the window and he grabbed my waist. Then

I was able to turn around the bed frame and use it as a shield. I avoided some heavy blows but crushed my fingers between the metal from the bed frame and the wall. Luna screamed, "Thief, I'm going to fuck you up!"

He wasn't able to kill me because of the strength I had from having carried so much sugarcane during my life. I brought the bed frame over him and he must've fallen on the floor along with it because I didn't feel any more hits. I jumped out the window and ran like a wild boar with no money, no Palmira, no nothing, and totally embarrassed that a derelict like Felipe Luna was calling me a thief.

I made it to the railroad tracks. I felt like I was going to die. The only thing I had was what I was wearing, no papers, nothing else, just like God brought me into the world. I caught the cargo train going to Santa Clara. I was down-in-the-dumps. I couldn't stop thinking about Palmira. There was nothing else on my mind. I couldn't even name the villages I went through. I arrived in Santa Clara with a swollen belly. I threw myself off the wagon and went to get a drink of water in the station.

Germán's brother's house was a stone's throw away from there. He was also a clown in a countryside circus. We knew each other. I looked and looked for him until it was really late. I asked all around for Morita the clown. I finally found him sitting in a doorway daydreaming. "This guy has no idea what's about to happen," I said to myself.

"Morita, do you recognize me?"

"Of course I do, Man. What are you doing here?"

"Morita, I'm going to tell you . . ."

I told him everything from beginning to end. No lies. He was familiar with the work and knew Felipe Luna was a snake. He didn't justify what I'd done, I'm not going to say that, but he had a good attitude towards me. Germán and I had gotten along well and they were very close. He gave me some advice, "Number one: Forget about Palmira. Number two: Get to Havana as fast as you can."

Number one was impossible. And I was going to tackle number two by selling some molasses candies his wife made. He gave me a board and the next day I covered almost every inch of Santa Clara selling those things. I sold the entire board in six hours. Since I wasn't familiar with the city, I'd walk aimlessly around from one side to the other. I'd even go down the same street a few times.

The park in Santa Clara is like a beehive. Whites on the inside; blacks on the outside. That's how the previous racist governments had them set up. It was legal. It was the same thing in other villages in the province. That's the way it was and nobody even said a word about it. Since I pass for white, although I'm only one quarter white, I put myself smack-dab in the middle of the white people and sold everything I had. Back then blacks didn't even have enough money to buy soap; how were they going to buy molasses candies?!

I had a thorn in my side for several days with the feeling that Felipe was looking for me. Morita's wife was much younger than he was. She helped him out. In the ring, she'd grab his instruments for him—Morita was in the band—and she'd give the bass a kick every once in a while. Her skin was like Palmira's, but she had bulging eyes and curly hair. She was the one who pressed the issue, "There's a rumor going around that you tried to jump Felipe."

Mail traveled fastest by mouth in those towns. News got to you first by mouth then later by foot. However, no one knew where I had disappeared to. She heard that I put a gun to his head and told him I'd kill him if he didn't give me the bundle of money. I was supposedly with another guy who looked like me, same color, same build, and Germán's little dogs jumped us. You name it, they said it! People are like that; they make up stories that aren't true out of nowhere. But no one talked about why I wanted to rob him or where I'd run off to. So I wasn't that worried. Regardless, I wasn't caught in the act. They had no proof. The only thing that's true is that I got into a messy situation there and nobody knew, not even by a long shot, under which banana plant I'd hidden.

I didn't know anything about Palmira. No one mentioned her.

Germán was very reserved and didn't talk. I was like a forgotten soul. Since I didn't have roots anywhere, people didn't know how to get a hold of me. They forgot about me overnight. My life during those years was all over the place, like a bird's life, one day perched on one branch and the next day on another. The only difference was that I caught cargo trains. If I'd had wings, another rooster would've sung.

Walking gets you going. I began trotting again. I was very blue because I left behind the sunshine of my life, but I was ready to finally make it to Havana. I made some money selling molasses candies. I bought myself a pair of pants and a coat and said to myself, "France surrendered, but I'm not." One thing led to another and before I knew it some time had gone by. I knew nothing about my family. I'd promised my sister I'd write her with my own hand instead of dictating words to people I didn't know. She believed in me. She knew I'd find my way sooner or later. Perhaps she never thought about the kind of work that I'd have to do because there in my village they didn't think about things. If you had a radio with batteries, you'd listen to romantic soap operas where everyone had a car. They didn't mention what happens in real life. The radio painted a really pretty picture for *guajiros*. So, when they'd go to the capital they'd feel every bump along the way.

The story about Venancio Prado is very sad. Venancio bought himself a radio with the money he made cutting sugarcane. Then he got hooked on adventure radio shows. He dreamed of being in Havana with a blond, a mill owner's daughter, who'd let him live like a king. False illusions! He got to the train station with a suitcase and straw hat and stayed in an all-male hotel on Revillagigedo Street close to Monte. He paid twenty cents for the first two nights, settled in and put his suitcase underneath the bed. Venancio must have thought "Attila against Rome!" when he saw all the hustle and bustle on the street, the trolleys, the modern cars, the parks full of people selling stuff and the most beautiful women in the world.

All of a sudden he saw a protest with people carrying red flags. He joined the crowd. They were communists asking for a raise and rights for dockworkers and tobacco rollers. In 1938, the Communist Party was legalized and that really set them off, and rightfully so. But Venancio didn't know what the heck was going on and got himself mixed up with that group of people who did know what they were doing.

So to make a long story short, Venancio got a beating . . . His legs swelled up like two flowerpots. He had to practically crawl to make it back to the flophouse. There he discovered that his suitcase had been stolen along with his straw hat. Luckily, he still had a five-peso bill in his pocket. It covered the trip back to Camajuaní. When he got there he started talking trash about the capital. Just to get him started, people would ask:

"So, Venancio, what did you think of Havana?"

He'd keep walking on his way to the sugarcane field, silent and not wanting to get involved in another quarrel ever again. Even in the hills of Guamuhaya they sang about Venancio's story in Havana. It went:

> *Venancio got to Havana*
> *his pockets full of gold*
> *bought himself a toilet.*
> *He dreamed of a Cubana*
> *to forget the plains*
> *but his dream was ill-fated.*
> *Water became salt*
> *and gold, fake metal,*
> *became Arabs' droppings.*

There are many stories about *guajiros* in Havana. Poor people who went there in search of a better life and instead they found filth and hunger. I saw many sketches in the Teatro Martí about a *guajiro* with a machete in his belt, a straw hat on his head, spitting in the street, and running away from cars like a cat on a roof. The theater was very misleading and made fun of the *guajiro*'s tragedy. It made a man from the countryside look like a clown from a cheap farce. They treated *gallegos* and blacks the same way. In my opinion, the theater wasn't guilty. It was those who thought like this and went to the theater to have a good time and applaud. Someone like me would see that show, laugh a little, and feel like crying afterwards because that was my blood, my family. That was me they were portraying and I couldn't curse out the authors of those pieces. Many of them have never even seen a *bohío*, or seen a belly full of parasites, or a woman giving birth in lowland foothills or in a row in the sugarcane fields because there was no way to get her to town. Those are the stories that make your hair stand on end.

What's the difference between the waves of *guajiros* that arrived in Havana without knowing how to read and write and the Hispanics who arrived here in New York in the 40s? Zero. They had the same fate. The same dog with a different collar. You can't fool me. I had two major clashes; the first with Havana, and then with New York. If I were born again my fate would probably be different, but it'd always have surprises. Despite everything, that's been my lifesaver given that I haven't been able to ask for anything more out of life. My grandmother Juana always said, "We poor people, to make things worse, don't die."

The bumps I hit could make a mountain as high as Pico Turquino in the Sierra Maestra, but I didn't let it get to me. I always thought of it as a pilgrimage. I didn't have time to get comfortable in any house or chair! One by one my grandmother's predictions came true. She always told me outright, "Your destiny is here today and there tomorrow. You carry an amulet made of mercury oxide in your pocket, Son." It has and always will be this way because I still don't feel settled living in New York and having an apartment.

My dream would be to return to Cuba, die there, and have them put Cuban soil on me. It's my last wish because Cuba is in my heart even here with the cold that's outside and inside. When I think about Cuba I cheer up a little. Cuba is like a person. When we, those of us who've been abroad for many years like myself, talk about her, it's as if we were talking about someone of flesh and bone. I don't want to talk just to talk, but it's not like this with other Hispanics. Cubans aren't satisfied with just memories of Cuba. I don't know anyone who didn't want to go back, even if it were just to visit his or her hometown. I can't think of one single person.

With the money I made selling molasses candy and the help of Germán's sister-in-law, I caught a train in Santa Clara and was really on my way this time. I said to myself, "No matter where you are, it's amazing what can make a poor man happy." Sitting on the train with some change in my pocket, heading to Havana, I was ready for anything. I'd left behind the only woman who I'd ever truly loved. But because things aren't always the way we'd like them to be, it was comforting to think that my dreams would come true in Havana.

It was a sunny day in October. Here in New York it's called autumn and there it's a typical summer day. The sun was so big that it covered the entire sky. An unbearable, liquid fire melted through the train's little window. I thought of the royal palm trees, the *bohíos* made out of them, and the seas of sugarcane and sickle bushes. I saw *guajiro* parents saying goodbye to bunches of kids at the stops and stations, and *colonos* wearing fine linen clothing and smoking luxury tobacco. There were also lots of old politicians with a gun in their belts or tucked into the back of their pants. Trains back then were moving advertisements. They had signs on them for hemorrhoid ointments like Quinina Bayol, Ironbeer Phosphate, Glostora, and OK Goméz Plata. Or announcements about upcoming radio shows on stations like RHC Cadena Azul or CMCX Radio La Casa Lavín. I surely felt that I was moving away from life in the countryside. The train's whistle was different in my village. When it went through a junction it was loud, it was a longer whistle. A real macho locomotive.

I got off at the first stop on the train line. People selling home-made sweets, tickets, and newspapers surrounded the passenger cars. For the first time in my life I felt drunk because I didn't know how to read. I'd have given an eye in order to be able to read *El País* and the front-page news about the German bombing of London. All the passengers were talking about it. I didn't want to admit that I didn't know how to read. I was sitting next to a barber from Havana. Luckily, he talked like a parrot. Thanks to him I found out what was happening in Havana. He knew a little bit about everything and he was a good conversationalist as every good barber should be. Barbers are the town teletypewriter. And this one wasn't any different. He had a curved nose, it looked like the hook you hang cows on. He didn't stop talking. He told me his entire life story. He went to his town twice a year to see his handicapped daughter and his mother who had just turned one hundred.

"You're in for a surprise," he said to me. "Havana isn't like people think it is. You'll break your back working."

"I know, but my back is like an elephant's and all I want to do is work."

I started to tell him about what I'd been through. Then he shut up.

"Look, I've heard it all before. You're no exception. Let's get real."

He promised to help me because he took a liking to me. He said, "When we get there I'll take you to the Palacio Cueto on Inquisidor and Muralla Streets. My brother works there."

I said, "Thank you." According to him the rooms were cheap and the place wasn't one of the worst.

Between one thing and another time flew by. The news about the war had all the passengers on alert. There was already talk that Cuba would enter the war back then. Someone confirmed it. Good things were waiting for me in Havana and in the middle of a world war. But I tried to make the best of it; if not, I'd have died an old man in my house.

Between talking about the London bombings, military service, and all that heavy stuff, we didn't even notice the dense smoke and smell of burning paper. We were caught in a fire. It started in the cargo wagon and made it to the passenger car destroying the wood. How did it start? No one had a clue. We had to stop in the town of Coliseo because the air from the track fueled the fire and we could've gone up in flames.

"My God!" I said to myself, "I'm back in hell!" The roof was on fire. Flames burned the cane seats and the signs hanging on the sides of the train. The cane crackled and the signs were falling off in pieces. So were the electrical wires. The barber and I helped the other passengers throw their trunks and suitcases out the windows. The speed of the flames was horrific. There wasn't time to think. With no time to spare, we grabbed our luggage, pushed down a door that was about to fall and threw ourselves into a bush. The train was going to burn on that hill of sickle bushes. You could feel the heat from the fire from where we were. A bright yellow glow covered everything. The passengers were terrified. They screamed, "We're alive! It's a miracle! We're alive! It's a miracle!" To me it was just another fire. It didn't surprise me. I was born into danger. Fear means nothing to me.

When all the sparks went out, the barber and I started to walk with our luggage towards to town of Coliseo. Soon we reached a pension with yellow doors. It reeked of crap and dampness. The filthy sign read "Hotel Modelo." Cockroaches and bedbugs swarmed the place and a lot of young couples were coming and going.

"We'll stay at a rooming house," the barber said.

"It doesn't matter to me," I answered.

We got as comfortable as we could in a bed barely made for one. All night we tossed and turned on top of the rock-hard mattress that stank like rotten eggs.

"Oh, Juana la Callá!" I kept telling myself, "what a big mouth you have!"

The next morning we waited for the ten o'clock train and we were on our way to the capital. We were like shipwrecked people with the pride of catastrophe survivors. The next day all the newspapers talked about the train fire. They even wrote that Colonel Fulgencio Batista's opposition was responsible because on that same day, October 10th, 1940, at twelve on the dot, he was elected President of the Republic.

3

The City

When it rains, it pours.

It was raining cats and dogs when the train pulled into the station. My dream had come true. It was the beginning of my new life. I dove right in. I was happy. Something finally worked out for me. I saw more flies than coconut candy in the station. A lot of beggars were sprawled out on the benches and platforms. I thought about Palmira and my sister Yara. They were the only two people I would've wanted to share that moment with. But I should forget about one and not write the other until I'm really on my own. I made a promise to myself.

"Well, Julián, we made it," the barber said to me. "Let's get something in our stomachs. Sound good?"

"Let's do it."

At a Chinese place a few blocks away we had hot chicken broth and shared a combination platter. It tasted divine! The place caught my attention because Chinese people ran it, but Cubans and Spaniards ate there. There wasn't even one Chinese person at a table.

When we left the joint we got caught in a sun shower on our way to Palacio Cueto. Only a couple of streets in Havana still had paving stones from the time of the Spaniards. Asphalt had taken over the city. There weren't even dirt streets anymore. For a *guajiro* like myself it was unbelievable to see smooth streets crowded with shiny automobiles and streetcars. Coal merchants and junk sellers were the only ones who still had horses. The noise in Havana was deafening, especially by the piers, because of the Mack trucks, cranes, and buses.

The rain didn't ease up. We reached Palacio Cueto drenched from head to toe. I wasn't going to be there for long. It was a good place on Muralla and Inquisidor Streets with a sink and a chifforobe in the room. It was thirteen pesos a month, but it was quiet and there were only a few cockroaches. I wanted to go out and see the world even if it was just for a second.

"Get comfortable for now and we'll see what's going on when the sun comes out," the barber said to me.

He walked down Muralla like the owner of a city he knew like the back of his hand. My excitement kept me going. I wanted to see the capital, especially on a day like that. It was October 11: the inauguration of the new president. And just like that, all soaking wet, I went aimlessly up Muralla. I ended up in Parque Central but the crowd and the shouting pushed me towards the doors of the Palacio Presidencial. I was sandwiched between bunches of people in the middle of a downpour. I looked for a place to sit down. I'd been standing for a while. When a tortoise wants to sit down, he puts out his hind limbs. I soon found a doorjamb next to the Iglesia del Ángel and got comfortable. A sheet of rain fell on my head. Rain when the sun's shining, just like in the countryside.

People were celebrating Batista's inauguration with signs, drums, and flying paper kites with razor blades attached to the tails. The voice over the loudspeakers was describing the entire ceremony. Laredo Brú handed over the presidential chair to a man who came out of the heart of the people. *El Indio*—that's what they called Batista—promised villas and castles during his electoral campaign. Everyone already knows what that degenerate did to Cuba. But at the time, the majority didn't know what he was capable of doing. We had come out of Gerardo Machado's dictatorship and we didn't think it could get any worse. Boy, were we naïve.

Batista went out on the north balcony of the palace covered by umbrellas. But before speaking, he stepped out from under the umbrellas in the downpour. Everyone applauded and cheered to the point of losing their voices. He lifted his arm as a sign of victory. He stayed like that for a minute in front of the microphones from the radio stations like RHC and CMCX La Casa Lavín. His wife Elisa Godínez could barely get close to him because of the crowds of supporters and journalists surrounding him. She couldn't give a damn about being First Lady. She'd been a washwoman and had many inferiority complexes.

The Casa Jabón Candado, a laundry soap manufacturer, had the largest banner at the event. It was a giant yellow soap that said "This is the man!" I could hardly hear Batista's speech because I was on one side of the park and the speakers carried the sound out to the bay. However, I did hear him scream "*Salud, salud!*" at the end. The rain didn't stop and his supporters stayed there to see him go off in a black car escorted by a squadron of horses. It was the same one he took to the palace from his house in Miramar. The military band played the national anthem and the director waved to Batista with his baton. National police patrol cars maneuvered in front of the palace. People were screaming as if they were possessed. I stayed sitting in the doorjamb until it was all over because I was stiff. When there was hardly anybody left on the Avenida de las Misiones, I started to walk over the signs, the cardboard popcorn containers, and the little September 4th flags.

A month after the fanfare, a tremendous stir brought me back to the park in front of the palace. The government had promised economic help to five hundred poor people and they never saw a dime of it. Vain promises! The people really believed Batista was going to clean up the mess, but he fooled them all. Crowds of beggars and people starving to death protested in front of the palace. It was a shameful display of rags and misery. The beggars brought empty condensed milk cans and raised them up towards the north terrace and balconies of the palace. They demanded food and work. They were there for hours and hours waiting for the president to come out and say something, anything. But Batista didn't even pop his head out.

When Prime Minister Carlos Saladrigas stuck his head out of a window to try to calm the people down, milk cans began to fly. An unemployed dockworker put a sombrero over his face, opened his arms and jumped from the fifth floor of an all-male hotel on Ayestarán Street with a sign on his chest saying: "Hungry. No work." To top it off, the only thing Batista did was talk about the new constitution.

The mulatto carpenter at Palacio Cueto was constantly praising his English. He was an old Batista supporter and his nickname was *Bembaecuchara*, or Spoon Lips. He'd tell the fools there they'd been friends in Banes. "Batista is an honorable man and he's going to do away with the Nazi party of Cuba." As if anyone cared. There were so few of them. They couldn't do a thing. Cuba was on the verge of entering the war, and on the side of the Americans. The rest was bullshit.

When it was dark and I was beat, I started to walk towards the hotel. That's when I realized just how big the capital really was. I'd never seen any place like it. When I saw the Capitolio, the Capitol Building, from a distance, it was like Havana was wearing a sombrero. It was bigger than the Palacio Presidencial. It stood out among all the other buildings. The Prado at the time smelled like a saddler's shop and a soap factory. The American tourists packed the doorways and bought crocodile skin wallets, perfume, and silk at wholesale prices. The Prado was a feast for the rich, but also a place for beggars, traveling salesmen, and kids selling lottery tickets. Before reaching Palacio Cueto, I bought a *frita*, a Cuban hamburger, and had an ice-cold *guarapo*, a sugarcane juice.

I collapsed on the bed. The next day at around ten in the morning the barber woke me up with good news. He had a job for me. In the classified section, they were looking for cooks or chauffeurs and I didn't know how to do either. I got lucky. I felt a great sense of happiness. Right away I went to meet the woman who owned

La Champagne. It was a hat shop on Monte and Someruelos Streets in the very heart of the shopping district. You never know who's going to help you out. Who would've known that someone I didn't know was going to help me out?

"Can he read?"

My heart skipped a beat when the owner asked the barber that question in front of everyone. I didn't say a word.

"He's as sharp as a razor. He'll learn in a flash, Matilde," he responded.

I started out mopping the floors and cleaning the glass. I was happy because I lived in a beehive. I was the only man. The old lady had lived through Weyler's Reconcentration and there wasn't a day that went by that she didn't mention it. She'd say that in Caraballo her family would dig a whole in the ground where they'd store crackers because everything was scarce. People starved to death. While dusting the glass, I'd hear Matilde's stories. The girls at the store didn't pay attention to her because they were tired of hearing the same thing over and over. But I was all ears so she wouldn't fire me. My goal was to be able to sleep in the hat shop at night. And it soon happened. I bought a cot and put all my clothes in a cardboard box and got comfortable in the backroom. Today I still yearn for the freedom I had there. It was the excitement of being young and the desire to find my place in the world. I disinfected the corner with creolin.

"You look like a cat," Matilde told me one morning when she saw me coming out of my cubbyhole. With my first paycheck, which was next to nothing, I bought myself a pair of white shoes and a can of Griffin liquid shoe polish to clean them. I sweated like a pig the first days. I'd get everything done in three hours.

Then I was promoted to hat delivery man. Since I couldn't read—although I was learning the letters—I'd carry a little piece of paper with the address on it and when I'd get close to my destination, I'd take out the paper and show it to someone. People must have thought: "This guy is deaf-and-dumb or retarted," I don't know how, but that's how with about twenty thousand setbacks I learned the streets of Havana in three months like the back of my hand.

I took my first reading classes with one of Matilde's clients, Mirita Bayo. She was the director of the center on Almendares Street. My feet also taught me how to read because I'd walk to the center every night. It was thirty blocks away. I'd save the money I'd have spent on the streetcar because my salary at the store wasn't even enough to buy a *frita*. Mirita was young, her skin was very pale and her hair was brown. She spoke with a Spanish accent because her parents were from Asturias. I'd dream about her all day. I liked that woman's legs a lot. I'd drool just looking at her. If I didn't see her one night, I'd feel bad. That's why I never missed class.

"Mirita Bayo! What a piece of work!"

I learned to read in the blink of an eye. I'd practice with the commercial billboards and the decals on streetcars. Sometimes I'd stop on a corner and spell out a brand of soft drinks or hair gel. People would stare at me and then practically run away thinking for sure I was a lunatic talking to myself in the middle of the street. I couldn't care less. I achieved my goal in less than a month.

"Well, Julián, it looks like you're free now."

I'd go eat fried plantains at the barber's house when things were tight. His wife loved me like a son. I'll never stop saying that sometimes a friend will do just as much for you as a relative, even more. Forty years have gone by and their daughter Mercedes and I still send each other Christmas cards. He died in 1960 trying to save the victims when "La Coubre" exploded.

At La Champagne I rubbed shoulders with Havana's high society. I especially met lots of people from Teatro Martí. They were well-off people, the daughters of mill owners, politicians, and businessmen. One of President Alfredo Zayas's sons was married to an artist from Teatro Martí and the two of them shopped there. She was always asking for me, but since I wasn't officially a salesman, I waited until she called my name several times. Then

Matilde promoted me from maintenance man, from organizing the boxes, to salesman.

Over time I learned the tricks. I'd pretend like I didn't see anything so that the customers would ask for me. My salary increase depended on it. It was clear: the female clients of La Champagne had their own style. They knew when they walked through the door what they wanted to buy: the color, the material, the type of flowers, the size. They already came with an idea, with something in mind. So the female employees just for kicks wanted to impose their style on them: "That color isn't in-style, Madam." They knew what they were talking about because they read all the fashion magazines that the store got. The clients didn't like it. What woman wants another one telling her what to wear? None! And because I knew about fashion, because I "yes"-ed them to death, I automatically became their favorite. Women don't want to hear another woman say to her: "That doesn't look good on you." However, a flattering comment from a man always means a lot. It didn't hurt me one bit to tell them all how beautiful they looked. So, what happened?

"Julián, come here."

"No, Julián, over here."

Matilde didn't have a choice. She had to put me behind the counter. But, I still continued scrubbing the floor, cleaning the glass, and running all over Havana delivering hats like a mad man. By winning over the clientele, I also won over Matilde. But it was different with my female co-workers at La Champagne. They saw that I was the customers' favorite and because they worked on a commission of twenty-five cents for each hat they sold, they started to mess with me. Never before in my life did I know just how wicked people could be until I saw what those women did. Some were seamstresses and others just saleswomen. All of them could pass for white. I was the only one who was a light-skinned mulatto in addition to being the customers' pet. The customers were chorus girls and women who, why not say it, would live off of married men's money. To be the sweetheart of a mayor, a city councilor or an orchestra director was a profession like any other in the Havana of those years. And there, as I said before, the crème de la crème would line up.

Matilde was the only one who liked me. The rest wanted me to vanish. They'd either put a piece of cake under my cot to attract ants or send me letters in death announcement envelopes to scare me. My family didn't have my address and they didn't even use death announcements in my town because no one knew what they were.

One day I put them in their place. It was getting to be too much. One of them called me over to fix the light bulb on her sewing machine because the switch was broken and when I went to fix it, she pricked me on the dick with a safety pin. I cursed her out right there, and then told each one of them to go to hell. "Kick me out of here. I don't care. I'll curse out all you bitches." Matilde came in the workshop frightened because I was raging. She told me I was right but said, "You have a very dirty mouth and these are hardworking women."

"Fine. Either they leave me alone or I'll go sell mangos."

She made me take care of the deliveries for about a couple of months. She got me away from that madhouse. I'd get back at six in the evening, so exhausted that I'd throw myself on the cot and fall asleep. Soon the tension eased because people eventually get used to everything. And they let their arm be twisted. I went back to the counter, assisting the customers.

"The crepe hat from China."

"The esparto veil."

"The satin ribbons."

"The velvet flowers."

It was nothing. I learned the business and when it came down to it, I knew more about hats than women.

Despite all the chaos surrounding me there, that's where I met a really pretty wool comber. She started to work there a few months after me. We did everything in secret so no one would find out. She was also from Caraballo. Matilde had brought her to try her out and because the poor girl was ignorant, she was paid pennies. It was so cruel! One day I asked her, "What's your monthly income, Honey?"

And she answered, "I don't have one. The agreement is that the *señora* pays me as I need it."

I promised to help her and I did. We made a terrible plan. We plotted against the old lady. That's when we began to fall in love. The other women kept an eye on the girl. They'd say things to each other like, "She came as a wool comber and she doesn't even know how to sew" or "She thinks she can become something smelling like dirt." She just wanted to live in peace and work, and send money to her siblings. A relative took a liking to her. She made her a loft on Sol Street and that's where she'd sleep without even a window to get some air.

"I like Havana," she'd tell me, "but I miss the countryside air. I can't breathe in this little room."

When you fall in love you start to give more and more. And because I don't think before I talk, I promised her a thousand things without thinking twice.

"Look, Emerlina, things will get better for us. You'll see."

"I don't believe you, Julián. Havana is very tough. And you're never going to get ahead there in the shop. It's not enough for two people to live off of."

"Have faith in me."

"Fine, Julián."

We were an item for longer than expected. I was really in love and so was she. I'd watch her glue the materials together, put on the flowers, and shape the hats. I thought she looked like a saint because she was quiet, very good, and had very soft, dainty hands. To be honest, they didn't look like they belonged to a woman born in the middle of the forest. We kept our thing a secret for more than a year, until I screwed her and she confided in Caridad Martín, the gossip queen. The next day the old lady found out about everything.

"Julián, I told you not to get involved with any of my employees."

"Matilde, I'm serious about Emerlina, I swear."

"But, you don't even have a pot to piss in, Julián. What do I tell her family?"

"Tell them that I'm marrying Emerlina."

The news about what had happened never made it to Caraballo. We were in a big mess. But in a nutshell, she was sixteen and I was twenty-one and we were both willing to deal with things. I promised Emerlina I'd marry her on the same day the Japanese attacked Pearl Harbor. We were alone in a room on Blanco Street. It belonged to a Lebanese woman who owned a variety store. She rented it to us for one peso. The nights we spent together there were divine. We thought that was a real home. Emerlina was the first woman I really lived with. And since being honest provides comfort, although it doesn't pay, I behaved like a man with her. I worked, rather we worked, to save money to get the wedding license. We saved up something and at least we managed to move together to an *accesoria*, a small ground-floor apartment on Zulueta Street.

I was really hot for her. If Emerlina went to unbutton her blouse, I started to get excited all over. It was that smooth, olive skin and those full lips and that black hair . . . everything about her made my blood boil. There's a difference between a fresh, ripe piece of fruit and a piece with a bite out of it. No one had ever touched her, no one had ever kissed her; I showed her everything with the little I knew. I would have wanted to get married for real. But the money wasn't there and we spent a lot on the *Aires Libres del Prado* hearing the all-female bands, going to the shows in Teatro Martí, going to La Concha beach, drinking beer, and being young since you only get one chance.

I don't think either one of us was obsessed with getting married. We liked each other, we loved each other and that was all. And since her family lived far away, it took them a while to find out that Emerlina was living with a man. I suffered a cruel blow when her brother, built like a beast, introduced himself to me in

La Champagne. First he called over Emerlina, who was sewing the headpieces that day and told her to get me. Because I was the only man there, he picked me out right away. When I saw her speaking with a man in the doorway I realized something strange was going on. She didn't have the guts to come in and get me. From the way her brother and I looked at each other, all the broody hens in the place realized what was going on. They would've stopped working if it hadn't been for Matilde who kept on top of them.

"Jacinto Pérez. I come on behalf of my sister's honor."

"Very well. We'll talk when I finish here, okay?"

"No, we'll talk now."

I remember that day and want to laugh. Especially when I think about those women dying to pop their heads up, busybodies under the old lady's whip. Jacinto waited until six in the afternoon because Emerlina begged him to. We started to walk and I told him I'd take him to our place on Zulueta, where we'd clear up everything. Luckily, Emerlina took charge. She knew her brother and how to deal with him. We opened a bottle of rum and I promised him, "I'm going to marry her."

"This is the man I love, Brother. Please understand."

Jacinto came to Havana to defend his sister's honor and for his own good. But things didn't turn out so badly. No blood was shed. And when Emerlina saw that we were already getting along like brothers and that we'd finished off half a bottle of Matusalem, she kneeled before the statue of the Virgin of Loreto that was behind the door and said, "*Virgincita*, you performed a miracle."

It was a miracle that I had to let Jacinto, your typical thug, sleep there on the floor, on a mat we borrowed from Eva la Libanesa— she was Lebanese. The following morning the three of us got to the store early, as expected. We opened because I was the one who had the key. And one by one those witches arrived. When they saw us conversing as if we'd always been the best of friends, as if nothing had happened, they pretended not to notice and started to talk out loud. We shut up.

"You handled yourself well," Matilde told me.

"I didn't do anything. It was Emerlina who calmed him down."

"And now what are you two going to do with him?"

Jacinto was still a teenager. He asked me to look for a job for him so I took him to meet Martín Palomas, the barber. He was a mess. For one month he was bumming around and sleeping in an all-male pension. We paid for everything, of course. With the help of the doorman at Teatro Martí, I found him slave work for which he was very poorly paid. It was a job I'd already done in countryside towns. Jacinto, the man sandwich, would go all over Havana advertising Niní Marshall movies and events at the Martí. He made enough to eat doing that, but it wasn't enough for a room. No one was going to tell me I had to get stuck with this guy! Emerlina, like the good sister she was, wanted to protect him, but I immediately saw the cunningness in his eyes and mentioned it to her.

"Something bad is going to happen to your brother in this city."

To make a long story short, Jacinto was stabbed thirteen times in a brawl on the way out of La Campana nightclub on the corner of Infanta and Manglar. Basically, he tried to get wise with the Indian boss of the mafia who controlled marijuana in the Victoria neighborhood, when he wasn't anything more than a little *guajiro* from the countryside who couldn't read and had a lot of straw in his head. We found out about it when his body already stank in the morgue. The manager of the pension, the same one where I'd lived, came to La Champagne with the news so that we'd go identify him. When I took the sheet off his face and saw his eyes wide open, I thought to myself: "Life sucks." My heart fell to the ground, because in spite of his faults, he'd been a poor soul trapped in a wolves' cave.

Banditry had invaded Havana. Every day you'd hear about people found dead on the street, gangs of thieves, gambling dens where one bloody fight lead to another and another. Basically, Havana was totally corrupt. Emerlina asked me to write a letter to her family explaining what had happened. It wasn't all that good, but no one could answer it anyway. And a week later, a man came to the store looking for me and told me that Emerlina's parents didn't want to believe it and that every day they'd go look for Jacinto at the train station and the Omnibus Aliados stop.

That memory of Havana in the 40s is very vivid in my imagination. And once in a while I think about it when I hear about crime on the Lower East Side or see, with my own eyes, atrocities like one about the gunmen in a car who pulled up in front of a Christopher Street bar and shot two men at close range who were going down the steps of an iron staircase, with no idea that they wouldn't make it to the sidewalk alive. That's why even when I was up to my neck in a violent situation I always tried to get out in time to save my ass.

It just so happened that I heard something about my family from Enelio Castro. Across from the *accesoria* on Zulueta, almost in the entrance, there was a billiard table with a kiosk that sold *bolita* numbers. The gamblers would spend the entire day there looking to double their money or waiting until their lucky numbers came out in the Chinese charade. Since we'd go in and out several times a day, we were used to hearing someone sing at the top of their lungs the lines: "It's a snake and doesn't crawl." "It's not a bra and it presses lumps." "It's a bug and doesn't bite." "It opens its tail and it's not a peacock." Between the clamor from the billiard table, charades, the *bolita*, and the Quintero sisters' sewing, our house was an ongoing circus. The entire neighborhood would gather there: the Chinese, wholesalers, bus drivers, Polish shoemakers. They'd play their number quietly and leave. Also the whores from the *cuarterías*, the decrepit rooming houses, across from the train station. Anyway, it was the whole neighborhood. They'd say all kinds of things to each other, all kinds of curses. But it never got ugly.

One of the Quintero sisters was married to a man from Asturias whose last name was Méndez. He was over six feet tall. When he'd slam his hand on the table anyone who was up to no good got out of there. If there was a fight, they'd shout all kinds of serious insults at each other, pull out knives, but Méndez would go over and ask, "Who's the tough guy here?"

And like peaceful doves they'd continue playing pool or slip away between the walls. The real tough guys would go fight by the walls of Havana or the train park.

"What goes around comes around! They're all bigmouths. They come to fuck with the business." That was Méndez's slogan.

I played Chinese charades a lot and won. My lucky numbers were: thirty-six, pipe; the last number of the Chinese list; and thirteen, peacock. But billiards would bore me and it was bad news no matter how you looked at it. I'd leave either destroyed or with a loose tooth.

Yara sent Enelio Castro to go see me at La Champagne, but the big idiot showed up there at seven in the evening. When he didn't see me, he started to ask around for me and the shoe shiner next door gave him my information. That night I found him at the door asking Petronila Quintero for Julián, the grandson of Juana la Callá. God is the ultimate fortuneteller. Enelio, the ultimate idiot. We hugged and were happy to see each other. He told me right away that my sister remarried and that she always showed my letter to everyone. My mother was the same as always: a woman who lived in another world, who didn't do anything else but cook and clean. But she was my mother, and I sent Enelio back with some things for her: money, shoes, Emerlina's clothes and gifts for my nieces and nephews, especially for Andrés, the oldest.

I took Enelio to Reina Mercedes because he developed a tumor on his belly. A doctor from Puerto Padre sent him to Havana to have it looked at. He didn't want to be operated on. He visited all the espiritista centers in Marianao. He left a few days later. We took him to the station, and when he got on the train Emerlina said to me, "If he gets there alive, it'll be a miracle."

We never saw Enelio Castro again.

The Quintero sisters, Regla and Petronila, set up a part of the game room where they'd sew. They'd make money on cheap materials that they'd dye with Dalía. In the corner there was an image of Las Mercedes with her eyes covered during the day so she wouldn't see "the workings" of the place. Below that Regla and Petronila had their Singer pedal sewing machines. They were known to be good seamstresses. They made bridal gowns and dresses for *quinceañera* parties, wedding veils, and their specialty was dressing dolls and fixing their hair.

It was a popular place because if you didn't stop by to play billiards or the *bolita*, you did to admire the Quintero sisters' work. They'd do everything: dye the fabric, iron it, dress the dolls, fix their hair, give them very long eyelashes, and polish their nails. In Emerlina's free time, she'd help them dress the dolls, while I'd pick up the scraps of fabrics and cigarette butts. We'd help in any way we could to thank them. We were paying seven pesos for a room with a bathroom. It was the last one in the house that was available. Méndez was good to us. Many weekends we'd go in his car to bars on Guanabo beach. He and Petrolina were not married, but they'd been together for over twenty years. Méndez was a fan of dark beer, like myself, and unstoppable at *cubilete*, a traditional Cuban game. He was proud of his woman. He'd say, "I wouldn't trade that mulatta for any other."

They'd treat each other like boyfriend and girlfriend. They'd been dating since the 40s. I spent about three years of my life between the hat shop and the *accesoria*. But one day I came down with a serious case of wanderlust when I least expected it. On a good day, after winning three hundred pesos on the lottery, I went with my woman to Saratoga Hotel and there at a table I told her, "I'm leaving La Champagne. I'm going to look for something else to try out something different."

Emerlina supported me in everything. I've never met a more devoted woman. I went to talk to the doorman at Teatro Martí to see if they were hiring. Things looked dim. The country's political situation was terrible. Batista had fooled the people and turned the Constitution into a piece of shit. Eddy Chibás started to broadcast his radio speeches on the air and really shook things up. There were unforgettable programs back then. Every single Cuban listened to them: Chibás's broadcasts with the saying "Honor versus money," borrowing it from the Boricuas, of course; *La Novela del Aire*; and later *El derecho de nacer* by Félix B. Caignet.

A famous cheap politician hid in Roland's Photography Studio and El Colorado, a hard-core gangster, riddled him with bullets in the back. Every day you'd hear about someone dying like that. I saw incredible things in Havana, things you'd never see in the countryside. The countryside is all about work, ignorance, and hunger. Havana was also about vice, prostitution, and many incredible stories. Eleven- or twelve-year-old girls, *pollitas*, chicks, who had just gotten there, would follow men around the streets offering to do all kinds of things to please them. There were occasional efforts to clean up the capital city. They'd manage to spread out the prostitutes by going where the working girls would gather. They'd temporarily close the bad neighborhoods. It was like the shit hit the fan. In other words, you could find *la mala vida* wherever you wanted; corruption and crime were all over the place.

One night Emerlina and I were coming back from a dance at La Tropical and we found Méndez standing in the door to the house cursing out Lieutenant Sandoval, "He's a pervert, an outlaw. He's going to pay for this."

It was in the middle of one of those clean-ups orchestrated by the politicians to put on a show. Ramón Grau San Martín was on the verge of becoming president of the Republic and Batista's followers wanted to go out with a bang. They liquidated thousands and thousands of gambling parlors and handcuffed many women who worked the kiosks and took them to the bivouac when the real owners and the ones in charge of the operation were their husbands. One day they carried Petronila away just like that to the bivouac. Regla hugged my woman and Emerlina, who had a saint's mouth, said to her, "Look, Regla, they're looking for money, that's all. Petronila will get out in two days, you'll see." In fact, they wanted Méndez to make his "contribution" to the district police, something that he didn't do deliberately because, although he was good to us, he was as cheap as they come.

Poor Petronila had never been in a place like that. You saw

everything there: big bullies, prostitutes, petty thieves, and even women accused of being involved with the mob. Most of them were very pretty. They looked at Méndez and me like they were begging for mercy. About four or five well-dressed women were leaving the room with lots of wooden benches. They moved them to a different place or let them go. We never found out. But the *boliteras*, the female operators of the numbers game, and the prostitutes in that pandemonium were in the dampest and filthiest corner of that building's basement. Méndez was carrying a stash of money in his pocket and was going to get his woman out of there even if it cost him an arm and a leg. I was the one who spoke to the officer: "I'm here for Petronila Quintero, resident of Zulueta Street . . ."

"Do you have the bail?"

"Yes."

Méndez painfully took out the two hundred and fifty pesos from his pocket and threw them on the folder.

"She's all yours!" the officer said to him.

Méndez didn't even answer. I looked into his eyes and felt like saying to him, "Bastard, you're jealous of the *gallego*!" The bivouac closed at eight in the evening. They shouted "Petronila Quintero!" so they wouldn't have to go down and get her. She came up to the first floor bars, squinting her eyes because of the bright fluorescent lights in her face. When we got out on the street Petronila, who was tough as nails, said, "Méndez, a cold shower. That's all I want."

A few days later the gambling parlor opened up again with Chinese and Indian charades. Méndez agreed to the "contribution" and the same policemen would go there to bet, and more confident than ever that the bank had solid backing. The authorities now protected Méndez. There was a rumor going around—I'm not sure about it though—that Castillo, Havana's most powerful banker, was personally involved with Méndez, and that he told him every once in a while a charade number. I'm never going to forget how that place was run. Among the billiard tables, the sewing machines, the threads, the colored fabric, the paper flowers, and the painted dolls, there were also Regla and Petronila's stories. When the door to the place would close at one in the morning they, being night owls, would prepare *café con leche* in giant mugs and start to tell stories about Havana.

"I know this city like the back of my hand."

"And what do you want me to say, Sweetie? I'm ten years older than you."

Emerlina would laugh and flatter them.

Their make-up and saffron-colored wigs made the two of them look more or less the same. When we moved out of there—a few days after Grau's inauguration—it was strange. And once in a while we'd stop by to have a coffee and hear them tell their stories. No one could tell stories like those two. Old Méndez would sleep in the back and his snoring would echo off the wooden walls of the billiard hall.

We grew up in Los Sitios neighborhood, close to Pontón. Our mother was an African queen in her previous life. Her clairvoyance made her come to that conclusion. During a séance on Concepción de la Valle Street she saw the crown on her head. The dead also told her. From then on her pains and needs didn't bother her. After all, as queen she'd had everything, and now, what could make her suffer?

My father was a dockworker on the piers and a baseball fan. He'd read the newspaper all day. And he was a catcher in Pontón. The world could be coming to an end and he wouldn't notice a thing. When they'd do a séance in my house, they'd shake my father from side to side, pour holy water on him, bless him, speak in his ear. And he, like a dummy, was mesmerized by the newspaper and wouldn't let go of it.

My mother's crown must have been copper because it was her favorite metal. She was a daughter of Oyá, the goddess of the cemetery and lightning. She'd say that the ashes of the earth were at one end of the rainbow and all the world's gold at the other.

Mamá had a girlfriend who'd sell fruits in the Plaza del Polvorín. They nicknamed her Luz de Yara because she had incredible revelations. She made a living off of *espiritismo* and the fruit stand. One day she saw a fireball and chased it all around Maloja Street with a bunch of people following her. When she got to the Palacio de Aldama across from the Parque de la Fraternidad the police grabbed her:

"*Señora*, what's wrong with you? What's wrong with you?"

"I saw it, I saw it. Take me to the Iglesia del Ángel."

The police let her go and the people went with her to the church. It was closed so on the stairs she started to bless everyone and screamed:

"I carry light, I carry light!"

Her son was a mess. His name was Cutico Flores and he didn't want to work in the plaza. He had what you call delusions of grandeur. And his mother didn't make the situation any better by telling him that he was a chosen one. He was thirteen and they still dressed him like a little kid and put a crucifix around his neck that went down to his belly. But all the good Cutico received came out bad. He never worked. He'd practice the chants on the roof of his house and wear old, moth-eaten suits. He looked more like a sultan than a gladiator.

Supposedly they even caught him dressed like a nun once, but gossip, I don't know . . . Well, when Angelina died, Cutico stopped singing. He spent months and months alone planting carnations and raising baby chicks on the roof. Mute and all alone he started losing weight and alienating himself from the entire neighborhood. My mother would stand up for him. Cutico would wash his hair three times a day and stand on the edge of the flat roof with a towel wrapped around his head. The neighborhood boys would call him a faggot and my mother, the saint that she was, would say to them: "No, kids, he's an artist, don't insult him."

Poor Cutico. He was already getting much older. One day,

this we did see, he put a crown of thorns on his head like Christ, covered his private parts with a loincloth and started to walk. Crowds followed him thinking that it was a joke or that he was dressing up for carnival. When he got to Café París he went up the stairs, oblivious to the shouts and jokes, and from the top floor of the building he jumped to the pavement without saying a word. When one of the waiters went to pick him up, he heard him say, "I took my life, I took my life," with a mouth full of blood.

Then there was the one about the two sisters Carmelinda and Luz. It was Regla's favorite:

Well, they were sisters just like any others, extremely close. The only thing that made them different from us was that they were twins. They lived to work and were good girls. They worked in the Public Works office and came here to sew because it was cheaper than in El Vedado. Everything was more expensive there. Carmelinda was more Type A than Luz. She took great care of herself, she didn't let herself go. Luz was not as stylish, more subdued. She loved children, animals, and tongue twisters. The two of them would sit in the doorway on I Street and since they dressed alike, from a distance you couldn't tell them apart. Luz would call over the kids, give them money and make them repeat the beautiful tongue twister that goes: "A certain young fellow named Beebee wished to marry a lady named Phoebe. 'But,' he said. 'I must see what the minister's fee be before Phoebe be Phoebe Beebee." They kids would have fun, and so would the sisters.

My sister and I would visit them several times so they could try on the clothes. We thought it was a shame to see women as respectable as they were taking the streetcar and subjecting themselves to that meat market. When we'd get there they'd always be rocking in their chairs or listening to radio shows in the doorway. I never heard them badmouth anyone. On the contrary, everything was: "How pretty you girls look!" or "Ernesto Galindo has such a beautiful voice, don't you think so?" When María Valero was run over by a car on Avenida del Puerto because she was looking at a kite, they swore never again to go over there. And they were at the funeral in the sun, hiding their tears behind dark glasses. They were saints, that's why Carmelinda ended up the way she did.

No one knew for sure where or how they met. He was an officer in the Navy, a brigadier I think, and married with children. His wife was very jealous despite the fact that he was already over fifty. She'd cast spells on him. Amparo, the daughter of Antolín el Bizco, Cross-eyed Antolín, was the one who prepared the potions for the officer's wife. Antolín was a *babalawo*, a priest, and she was a *santera*, a priestess. Amparo's son Eugenio told me that his mother would prepare a mixture of urine and toenail ashes for her. The woman put her own bodily fluids in it and gave it to the officer to drink with his breakfast. But she couldn't even tie him down with that.

Like a fool he fell in love with Carmelinda. And no one knew anything until they went out with a bang. Luz testified in the trial that her sister was a young lady, she swore. But she did admit that it had been a few months since she started coming home late and that she would tell her she'd gone to bring some little gifts to the nuns at Purísima Sangre.

Carmelinda fell under the claws of that swine. He had his way with her without even considering that she was like a child because she'd never been with a man. I'm sure he promised her marriage. He must have told her all kinds of things. And she believed him. It's true that it's sad to be single. I see my own sister with Méndez and it's different. She's happier than I am, more relaxed, she's always up for something. I'm very lonely . . .

Well, back to what I was saying. Carmelinda got into a motorboat with that swine at the marina and they went out to sea, out to the sandbar. They went with a captain, of course, and he was the one who told it all. In the middle of the sea they started to play dirty—when I think about it, I can't believe it—and the officer died of a massive heart attack. Carmelinda started to scream and ran out of the cabin like a crazy person saying she was going to throw herself in the sea so the sharks would eat her. The helmsmen calmed her down. He told her, "Pinch his eyes with pins to see if he's really dead." Carmelinda did it and the man didn't react. He was as dead as a doornail. Poor woman!

She got to the port with her leg tied to the bed. I can't imagine what she must have felt upon seeing that man coming out of the cabin stiff in the arms of the captain. She adored him. I can't imagine. The wall was filled with people and she was terrified. How horrible! The officer's family members bribed the press to keep it quiet, but the news spilled like beans all over the entire island and it was in the police blotter of the Havana newspapers. We, because we didn't have the need to always look innocent, went to the trial to support our girlfriends. I don't know which one suffered more. At least Luz testified. Carmelinda didn't even shed a tear. She looked like Our Lady of Sorrows.

She carried out her house arrest with admirable strength. She never answered the telephone nor went out to stand in the doorway. One day we called the house and Luz asked us to forgive them, but they weren't receiving people yet. The two of them suffered a lot, but Luz dealt with all the blasphemies. She continued to sit in the doorway with the kids, although they often shouted at her, "Whore, assassin!" and a thousand other things. Since she was Carmelinda's twin, the bad people who passed by there confused the two. Cusita Estévez would do their errands and cook for them. She used to live here in Picota. She'd tell us that Carmelinda would spend her days crying behind the window and begging her sister on her knees not to go sit in the doorway.

You'd hear those stories and even cruder ones all the time at Regla and Petronila's house. That's what Emerlina and I missed when we moved out of there. Forewarned is forearmed. Méndez was not a bad guy but he was very greedy. Billiards and the kiosk weren't enough for him; he wanted to control it all. The Auténticos—The Cuban Revolutionary Party-Auténtico—, led by Grau, started to loot businesses and take control of customs. Méndez got a position as "customs inspector" through a city councilor friend and then dedicated himself entirely to smuggling wristwatches and drugs: opium packed in tea bags from China.

Emerlina got scared of what he was doing. I listened to her. The dividends Méndez had with the police were already pretty significant. They'd treat him like a gentleman and play billiards without paying a dime. I didn't like that way of doing things because all my life I've been a fighter. You end up paying for these kinds of immoral acts in the long run. If not, then how do you explain why every once in a while a big fish is killed on a corner and gangs start to form all over the city. No, I didn't get involved in that nonsense. Emerlina helped me and I listened to her. It killed us to say goodbye to Regla and Petronila. Méndez was happy because a room had opened up in his place. Not to mention that it was in the back with its own entrance for his business.

For two more pesos we found a room with a private bathroom in a *solar*, the kind you can walk through, on Virtudes almost at the corner of Blanco Street. A *solar* is something like a tenement house. Eva la Libanesa bought six rooms there and offered us one, considering we were friends and all. Good-time girls lived in the rest of the rooms, which were all smaller than ours. They worked in that area, the Colón neighborhood. People made fun of those street names. It was completely ironic that so many prostitutes lived on Virtudes and Blanco, Virtues and White in English.

Emerlina and I were comfortable there. The room was bigger than the one on Zulueta and we always had water. The good-time girls would sleep until two or three in the afternoon. They were hardly ever there; just the time it would take them to make lunch and bathe. At six in the evening they'd head for the *bayuses*; in the dictionary it also says they're called brothels or bordellos. They didn't bother anybody. And they were very considerate towards Emerlina. They always let her wash and hang her clothes in the hallway first.

The pimps would pop their heads in once in a while to pick a fight and the girls wouldn't take any shit from them. It was something else. Those guys were loud mouths and showy. They acted so smooth and were always with some old guy or some Yankee marine. Two beautiful sisters Felicitas and Cuba from Güira de Melena lived in room six. Cuba worked in a brothel on Jovellar Street and Felicitas would get business from the people in show business. Those two sisters got along with each other really well. I'd write letters for them to their mother in Güira. But the mother would only send telegrams saying, "We are fine health wise. I received the letter. Mima."

Felicitas was younger. She must have been about twenty-one or twenty-two. They were close-knit. There was a six-year difference between the two of them. Cuba would wash, iron, cook. She did it all. Felicitas loved to cut out photos of artists from the magazines back then. She'd ask me to write letters to Libertad Lamarque and Jorge Negrete so they'd send her autographed pictures of themselves. Their room was upstairs. You got up there by a spiral staircase that was really shaky. I'd always go with Emerlina to write the letters for them. The scent of Rhum Quinquina, a magic potion that got rid of dandruff, by Crusellas was impregnated in everything. The walls were covered with photos of ballerinas, popular bands, and tango and ranchera singers. Felicitas had a box from the department store El Encanto full of postcards from her girlfriends who'd gone to Panama, Guatemala, or Mexico to be in some sort of vaudeville shows. I don't know how it happened, but one day Felicitas grabbed a suitcase—it would be a "jumbo-size" here in New York—and she put it in the middle of the patio.

"Julián, Julián!" she yelled, "take this upstairs for me, please."

I took the suitcase upstairs for her. It weighed quite a lot completely empty. When it was packed, a strange man with a Panama hat and highly polished shoes picked it up, and put it in a latest model, small white bus along with Felicitas. She didn't say goodbye to us because we really weren't that close, but within a few days Cuba confessed to us that her sister was going to be in films in Mexico as an extra in Indio Fernández's movies.

"What type of film would that be?" my woman asked me.

And I told her, "Don't say a word when you see that woman in the patio. Don't even look at her too much."

Cuba started to receive telegrams and money orders from the Yucatán. The room became completely covered with photos of Felicitas in bathing suits posing for Churubusco Studios. She really made it.

"I'm also leaving soon," Cuba told us one day. She was sure of it. The swine of the house made fun of her. While she'd wash her clothes they'd shout all kinds of obscenities at her out of envy and because she wouldn't talk to anybody. Cuba would smoke fat, black cigarettes called Bock, which had already stained her teeth. She wasn't into show business, but she kept the room the way her sister had left it. During carnival she'd put on a green turban and be the favorite of La Sultana *comparsa*, the dance procession, from the Colón neighborhood.

She never got to go to Mexico or anywhere else for that matter. About a year after her sister had left, on the same day that Franklin D. Roosevelt died, she received the news from a musician in the sextet Embeleso that Felicitas was killed in a bullring in the middle of a shootout and that they'd buried her in a cemetery in Mérida. Then, darker and more horrifying versions came out. Happiness never returned to Cuba's eyes. Even though they were very close sisters, she'd say that Felicitas did it to herself. Emerlina and I didn't go up to room six as much anymore. We saw Cuba take down the photos of the artists from the walls. She threw them in the garbage and filled the room with Chinese calendars and saint cards. She had an older man staying there. He seemed pretty decent and based on what we could see, it looked like she retired from *la mala vida*. She was already over thirty.

One day my nephew Andrés, my sister Yara's oldest child, unexpectedly showed up at my house. Since it had been a billion years since I'd last seen him, I didn't even recognize him. It was like meeting him for the first time. He thanked me for the gifts that I'd sent him with Enelio Castro. He didn't know anything else about Enelio either. I'm sure he went to die in the countryside with his family, as did many *guajiros* from there. Into the forest. Andrés came with his stepfather, Yara's second husband, to work for a cheese and milk business. It was a big company.

I spent a couple of hours with them and that's how I found out more about my family. Few improvements and a lot of kids from both Yara and Pascual, my younger brother. Everything else was the same. I gave him some clothes from Machetazo. I felt like I got along with them, at least with my nephew. I said goodbye to them at Hotel Isla and went home. I got the impression that Yara's husband was a good man. I walked down the Prado among the balloons and streamers. I was happy about my family's visit. Celebrations in Havana were like huge parties with all your friends. Cars honking their horns and people hugging each other in the streets. World War II had ended with the Allied victory. People sang on the streets, "*Pin, pin, cayó Berlin. Pon, Pon, cayó Japón*," or "Berlin fell, pin, pin. Japan fell, pan, pan."

Cubans are really strong. That's why they've survived more storms than a jiquí tree. That's a timber tree with hard wood. Nothing destroys us. Many people got rich during the war. Organized crime was all over the place. There was a second round of big fish, although each time the fish were bigger, and fewer. The poor were still starving to death. The destitute neighborhood of Las Yaguas spread like the plague and almost reached the hills of Atarés. Chibás was the only civic-minded person. He founded the Partido del Pueblo Cubano, otherwise known as the Partido

Ortodoxo, to better the country. He'd speak anywhere and everywhere. He didn't care if he was on a platform or the hood of an automobile or in the middle of the street. He reached the people with his slogan "Honor versus money" and created a party that had many followers and was popular with women. The best men of the 26th of July Movement came from there.

In 1951, I felt the impact of his final speech known as Último Aldabonazo, the Last Call, here in New York. I really began to think about things. I was attracted to his new ideas about justice and reorganization. I befriended some members of the PSP, the Partido Socialista Popular, and the Partido Ortodoxo. They were ordinary folks who worked at dry cleaners, warehouses, and radio stations.

My girl and I went to some of Chibás's meetings on Avenida del Puerto and by the exit of CMQ television station at Monte and the Prado. She was such a big fan of Eddy Chibás. One day she saw him and he shook her hand and she swore to never wash it again. When I realized she wasn't joking—she'd only put her left hand under the facet—I made her stick both hands under the water and screamed furiously at her, "Damn it! Shit! Don't mix politics with fanaticism!" She was surprised because I'd never been violent with her in that way. I'll admit it was a radical way to deal with the situation.

"This isn't enough for two to live off of, Julián."

And she was right. My girl was very organized. She managed the household budget and realized that with the price increase throughout the country, what we earned wouldn't be enough to have a child.

"It's not enough, Julián, it's just not enough."

With her voice ringing in my ear I went to see the doorman at Teatro Martí. He was a good friend of mine who I knew from going out in Havana. He was originally from Oriente like myself. He had also taken great risks in life. I said to him, "Look, Ñico, my woman and I want to have a family and the two of us can barely live off of what we make at La Champagne. Let me know if you hear of something."

He knew everyone in Havana. He'd see them all line up at the opening of the zarzuela or vernacular theater seasons at the Martí. He promised to help me and all my hopes were centered on him. The old lady was not going to increase my salary nor was she going to let me be the only salesman. Emerlina got a percentage of what they made. She was the unhappiest person there because she was from Carabello and half related to Matilde. I put up with it all for a few months. Every night my girl and I would go drink rum with Ñico at a bar called Puerto de Tierra very close to the Martí.

"Julián, you trust Ñico too much. Months have gone by and nothing's happened."

"Do you want me to sell tickets on the street?"

"It's not that, but it seems to me that he's jerking you around and . . ."

Women are very astute and very distrustful. And you always have to hear it from them. However, this time I trusted Ñico. And there was a reason for it. One night, when the Martí was closing and the chorus singers were scattering out the side doors to catch the last streetcar, I run into Ñico. He hugs me with a big smile and says, "Julián, tonight we're going to get a drink at the Saratoga."

"What's this all about?" my woman asked him.

"It's because we're really going to talk now."

Ñico had spoken with the manager of RHC Cadena Azul and asked him for a job for me. The man said there was the doorman position if I wouldn't consider it beneath myself to clean the studio glass and supervise the vote count at the singing competitions and fan programs. I waited two days. It was the sensible thing to do in order to not to pester my friend. Then I asked him to take me to meet the manager. I put on my best: white shoes, a suit, and an Omega wristwatch that I bought from Méndez for thirty pesos. The guy checked me out from head to toe and asked me only one question bluntly, "Are you a heavy or light sleeper?"

"Light," I answered right away.

"Very well, then. You'll make seventy-five pesos a month. Are you interested?"

"Yes, I am."

He gave me a voucher to buy the uniform and the shoes. I felt like I entered the world through the front door.

"Now, how about a hot meal," my friend Ñico said to me laughing while we crossed Parque Central.

With the uniform package in my hand I went to see Matilde. The women who worked in the hat shop found it strange that I got there late that day. My girl read in my eyes what I wanted to say to her. She understood well and Matilde, an old woman who was very wary of life, said to me, "I suspected you wanted to leave. I already had the word out about the position for a replacement. Someone also from Caraballo. Don't worry, Julián, Emerlina will stay."

"In five years you didn't give me one raise."

"What raise are you talking about, Julián? I'm the one who knows this business. Go do your thing and have a nice life."

At RHC I found out what the human species was all about. I wish I had been a writer so I could've told what was stirring in that world among corduroy curtains and standing microphones. A real zoo of beautiful animals. But, why not say it, hungry and voracious for fame. I was going to see it all with them. They'd fight with each other to get into a studio. They'd argue and say they were going to kill each other to be first in line. Sometimes at four in the morning there would already be people sitting in the Prado. They were mostly women who wanted to get in on time to see any old artist perform. They were the years of Hugo del Carril and Rita Montaner. They even offered me money so I'd let them line up in the studios or say Mr. or Mrs. So-and-So was first in line. The doorman saw everything. He'd take it all in and later draw his own conclusions.

La Muertaviva was the most popular character. She'd collect autographs and match boxes with photos of artists. Her hair was white, but she'd wear a beret on the grayest part. That's how she hid her age. She'd use *tú* with the artists; speak with them as if she'd always been their best friend. She'd bring them boxes of cigarettes and bars of *dulce de leche*. And there wasn't anybody who'd snatch her spot in the door to the broadcasting station. She'd really stand up to the others. But they respected her. She'd be walking very slowly when she got there and instead of asking who was last in line, she'd say to the people in their ear, "Let me by, please." And everyone would be really confused because she was the last person to get there. Just like that. It was just one of those things. She'd move to the very front and look discretely towards the back and say, "Thank you."

Since the management knew about her, they didn't pay attention to these things. By the time I started there, she was already part of the tradition. Seeing that I was a new face, she came and said to me, "If you're new here, I'll let you know that I'm the founder of this station."

I smiled at her. She didn't speak to me after that. There was no reason to. Everyone knew and respected La Muertaviva. Sometimes they'd make fun of her because she was extremely skinny and she'd put loads of powder on her face. But if someone tried to take her place or argue with her someone would come to her defense from somewhere in the Prado, from behind a tree or a light post, or from a hallway. "Leave the lady alone." La Muertaviva would even ask the sound technicians and the electricians for an autograph.

Working at RHC was really like being in the heart of it all in the capital city. That's where I learned about politicking during those years in Cuba. I found out what an Indian boss was really like: Amado Trinidad Velazco, the owner of the broadcasting station, a cacique in a linen guayabera. My God, what a guy to sweet talk the people! If someone in Cuba symbolized the new rich it was that *guajiro* with an emperor's swelled head. He was arrogant, a crowd pleaser. He became a dragon. He hoarded many businesses and controlled the lives of many artists. He'd put them up on a throne and later let them fall. I saw young singers, very young, pretty girls, show up there with a tremendous desire to sing. They weren't even able to open their mouths. However, others with hoarse voices and turtle bodies rose up like foam because he thought they were funny or because someone recommended them. They were simply housewives with nothing but air in their heads. The radio business in Cuba was very dirty. The owners of the broadcasting stations, like Amado Trinidad and Goar Mestre, would compete to fuck with each other. Amado was the man with the guayabera and tobacco and he had his audience. Mestre was an idiot son of the Americans.

In the Parque de los Enamorados, where the statue of Luz y Caballero is, some magnificent groups would get together in the afternoons. That's where the ones who aspired to sing on the station and who hadn't had the opportunity, or the magic wand hadn't touched them, would get together. Taking turns, they'd sing everything, they'd try voices, exchange music scores of famous songs like *Granada*, *Estrellita* or the tango *Uno* first sung by Rita Montaner a few days after I started working at RHC.

The government of Grau was on the way out. It was totally discredited. Robbery was increasing. Orlando Lemus, El Colorado as they called him, was competing with Lucky Luciano. He killed a lot of people during the governments of both Grau and Prío. He'd come to the broadcasting station with his gun; he was a janissary. They say he took money from Amado Trinidad. He trafficked drugs and weapons and became powerful during the years after Grau because of his personal relationship with the Prío brothers.

Nothing was a secret at RHC. Whoever wanted to, got bribes from "the shepardess." Whoever didn't want to, calmly stayed in his place, waiting for his paycheck at the end of the month. Not everyone was lucky enough to win the lottery. The Cuban Army Chief of Staff, Genovevo Pérez Dámera, won fifty thousand pesos. He said he'd put them in his bank account because he wasn't spendthrift. To say that, during those years, was to make fun of the people. Genovevo and his buddy, José Manuel Alemán, a Batista supporter who reached Grau's government with lots of drive, made a killing during those years. Alemán became a pal of the First Lady Paulina Alsina and robbed her with both hands. He'd give his buddies wallets full of bills. Chibás was one of the spokesmen of the opposition party. And the communist leaders, Lázaro Peña and Blas Roca, also condemned the immoral acts.

I remember this like it was yesterday. Hitmen shot at a group of students from the Instituto de La Habana that was meeting in the Asociación. They were gangsters and murderers brought together to form what was called the BAGA, a repressive apparatus created by Grau to impose his will with force. They killed the student Carlos Martínez with a single bullet in the middle of his chest. And they wanted to hide it from the press. The students totally turned their back on the government. They paraded through the Prado towards the Palacio Presidencial and when they passed the broadcasting station they screamed:

"Grau, you murderer. Die Alemán!"

"King Kong, out of there Ramón!"

With thunder like that there was no way you could think that Grau would be re-elected. And just like how the story about the Capitolio Diamond was kept in the dark—because everyone suspected that Alemán was the one who stole it to give it to Paulina—Grau's prestige was really low like a pile of mud.

Finally, and to say goodbye to him with a gold broche, they gave him an homage and the students covered the Alma Mater with a black cloth. That homage was the most ridiculous thing in the world. The pasquinades said, "Grau opened the path to glory for the people." Meanwhile Chibás condemned the possible reelection. Havana crackled during those days. The organizer of the homage spoke from the RHC microphones. He said, "The blue waves of this illustrious broadcasting station, bring to you the tribute that the people will give their national hero, Doctor Ramón Grau San Martín. We have to ask him, cry to him if necessary, that he continues in the presidency." It was disgusting. Someone wanted to use the same Guanabacoa platform that Martí had used to fight the Spanish government to pay homage to Grau. The scandal grew. Grau came out of the palace saying, "I go as I came."

And Chibás sarcastically added, "He came in with a cyclone and goes out with another. Good riddance!"

Grau entered the presidency with a very big cyclone and left in the middle of another that also caused a lot of havoc. It turned again and Millás, the meteorologist from Casablanca, broadcasted wrong forecasts. To sum it up, Grau, just like Prío, was two cyclones for Cuba. No one suspected such a disgrace. And a lot less that they'd disappoint the people like they did. Grau announced an agrarian reform. But the people to make fun of the famous measure would say the land was distributed in little bags.

Carlos Prío Socarrás's inauguration on October 10th, 1948 caught me in middle of a family tragedy. My woman miscarried an almost four-month-old baby boy after we'd built up the courage to have him. The two of us were excited. We knew it was going to be hard. To have a child at the time was risky, but Emerlina wanted it. She did everything possible to get pregnant and then to save it. But everything came tumbling down.

The broadcasting station transmitted a program called *El Torneo del Saber, The Tournament of Knowledge*, on Saturdays at nine minutes after noon. People would send in a question and if the committee or the studio audience couldn't answer it, the sender would win five pesos. I sent in the first questions under my woman's name so that it wouldn't look suspicious and snuck them in the hat with a password. The program coordinator was in on it. We asked all kinds of things. What was María Valero's real name? How many teeth does a shark have? Who killed baby Celia? Things of that nature. We won about thirty pesos that we shared with the coordinator.

We'd do that trick every once in a while using made-up names. That way we were able to ease the pressure a little bit in order to get by. And we were excited about the child. In order to get pregnant Emerlina did the incredible. She went to see a black woman named Guillermina Palacios from the Juanelo neighborhood. Guillermina said to her, "You're going to have identical twins, you'll see. Name them Cosme and Damián."

The black woman made my woman believe many strange things. She told her, "You and your man are going to be very rich. You're going to live outside of Cuba for many years. Your children are going to be doctors and lawyers."

Every day Emerlina would come home to me with another episode of a soap opera on the radio. Just like forty-four whales appeared off the coast of Florida in early October, Guillermina's house was filled with believers. She had said the sea was going to return the spirit of the dead to the coasts and that when it happened, it would be necessary to pray and cleanse. The believers, frightened, thought that it was the warning.

"It's the Virgen de Regla. She's furious because of all the murders and robberies," my girl would say over and over.

I think the cyclone that brought Prío to the presidential seat wiped everything out. There were more than fifteen dead and hundreds wounded in Havana. More than eighty boats sank, even though the president's was the only one printed in the newspaper. It didn't matter. It was the same as always. Millás didn't do anything right. However, Guillermina, that old lady, had predicted a cyclone for those days. What a coincidence!

When my woman went to see her in Juanelo to tell her to her face about the miscarriage of our son, Guillermina gave her one of her typical answers, "Look, My Dear, what happened is good. Anyway, I told you that they were going to be twins, didn't I?"

Guillermina's grandparents were slaves. She was always ready and willing. She always had tobacco in her mouth and a little white handkerchief in her left hand. She'd say, her grandmother, when she died, flew to Guinea because of all she had suffered from the whippings she got on her back with her face down in the dirt during slavery. According to her, the entire work gang had seen her rise up over the sugarcane plantation.

I got Emerlina out of there because if not, she'd have driven me crazy. Between the soap operas, the *espiritismo*, and the Hugo del Carril performances in the Martí, our life was going down a bad path. I wanted to earn some more money and get her out of the hat shop, but it was impossible. I'd look up and the sky was overcast. I'd look down and the road was pure stone. There was nothing I could do. Havana was a city for puppeteers, politicians, players, and "*botelleros*" who collected a salary from the government and didn't do that kind of work. Prío's hobby was buying *fincas*, country homes, and sugar mills. He ordered a personal airport to be built on his *finca* in Bahía Honda and toilets dipped in gold for his two mansions in La Chata de Arroyo Naranjo.

Things weren't really going well for me. It was one thing after another. That's when I met Miguelito Cuesta through Ñico. Miguelito was a black telephone, very sharp, and a lynx at getting out of trouble. He'd been a dockworker and really admired Aracelio Iglesias, the best-known leader of the Havana docks. It's worth mentioning, and this isn't news to anybody, that during his first days in office, Prío Socarrás ordered to have Aracelio killed. Miguelito lived in downtown Havana at 205 Paula Street in a *solar* called El Chorro because the sewer water and the shit would flow out of there in streams. He became a regular at the broadcasting station. His woman and mine became good friends. She was a very quiet, black woman, half *espiritista* as well, but she wouldn't consult for just anyone. She'd always be saying, "I can't go out because I have to get the stain off of Miguelito's guayabera."

The poor man only had one guayabera and she'd wash it for him every day. Ñico would give us tickets for the shows at the Martí when we felt like going. That's how we saw Garrido and Piñero in *La toma de posesión*. A show that made fun of everything. It'd make fun of the day that Prío became president. We also saw the Agustín Rodríguez Theater Company and many Spanish and Argentine artists. In *La toma de posesión*, there was a jingle that people learned from hearing it so much:

Prío says it's one way
I say it's another
but I want to put on record
without trying to compete
that in this case
I'll stick with my way.

People didn't have any faith. Prío asked Washington for a very large loan. He was going to mortgage the country. He boasted that the Partido Auténtico hadn't received a penny from abroad. People were in the streets were struggling to get by and he was there with his vices and banquets.

"What you want is a kid, a boy."

"Of course, I want a boy, a tough boy."

Miguelito livened up our lives. Finding a personality like his in the middle of a storm would cheer up a dead person.

"With what you know, with what you've lived, with the stunts you've done, you should be a tap dancer at the broadcasting station and not a doorman."

I didn't want to go back to the adventurous life I had in the circus. I wanted stability so that I could have a house with a furniture set and a family. But fire had marked my days. Because when I wanted to force myself to do something it was impossible. It's as if I had *ají guaguao*, a pepper plant, in my pants. There's never a way for me to feel settled.

Miguelito tried to make me his partner. And he started to give me tap-dance lessons. He was stuck on becoming a duo. Emerlina would laugh because I was rusty and couldn't even get the down-up, down-up shuffle. But I wanted to help him and using the little pull I had, I got him in the line-up at the broadcasting station. Miguelito, although he was a little foolish, did sing boleros and guarachas and didn't do a bad job.

He started singing as an amateur in a parody of Jabón Candado to the music of *La guantanamera* by Joseíto Fernández. I introduced him to some important artists: Orlando de la Rosa, the composer; Manuel Urquiza, the broadcaster; Paul Díaz; Mario Barral . . . They took a liking to him because he was jolly and had a good ear for music. Then he'd sit on a bench in the Prado with Ñico and a remarkable claque would gather within minutes. The people who'd go to the radio programs would request songs and Miguelito would sing and tap dance on the benches along the walkway.

Or he'd be telling crazy stories, like the one about his great-grandmother Mercedes, a very pretty, heavy black woman. Her master was crazy about her. But Mercedes hated him. One day he called her to go to bed with her in the house of the mayoral, the overseer of the sugar mill. Mercedes went because she was a slave, but when she lifted her skirt, a *veintiuno*, or rather, a black boa was twisting around her waist. When her master saw it, he ran around the sugar mill screaming.

The rumbas played there made history. Miguelito would start singing and it reached the people all the way up the Prado to Café de Galiano y Lagunas. It was the place where all the show-business people would always go back then. I'd get off of work and run there. Sometimes I'd bring Emerlina with me or run into a party girl and we'd have a blast.

One day Rita Montaner showed up there. She came with her husband, a lawyer from Camagüey, and *Mamita siento un bombo*. Mamita's name in real life was María Auxiliadora. She was always with Rita. When Rita would go on tour, she'd hit the first artist who got in the way. She was crazy about the show-business people. Mamita was a light-skinned mulatta. She'd wear bright red lipstick. If Rita told her to jump off a bridge, she'd do it. I remember that night as if it were today. She went with Rita to the police station. Rita was a difficult person. One day she'd say hello to you when she got to the broadcasting station and the next she wouldn't even look at you. If she said hello to me, I answered her. And if she didn't look at me, I didn't look at her because she was capable of saying anything.

A young mulatta started to sing stuff from her repertoire on the Pinilla Rum show. So she showed up at the studio one night. When the girl came out from behind the curtain with a little cage of *zunzunes,* or bee-humming birds, to sing the famous *pregón,* that's a special Cuban song, by Ernesto Lecuona, *Vendedor de pájaros,* Rita came up to the stage, with a thunderous ovation. She asked the girl for the little cage and started to sing the number. People heard her say to the girl just starting out: "Get the hell out of here."That's the way she was and people placed her on an altar.

The artists from RHC would go to Galiano Café a lot. Rita poked her head in there once in a while. She was the prettiest mulatta in the world, and also the one with the loosest tongue. The name *Lengualisa,* Smooth Tongue, fit her perfectly. It was the main character's name of *La Chismosa,* Gossip, a show that denounced the robberies and banditry of the Grau government.

When Rita showed up at that neighborhood café it was a big deal. Since I lived two blocks away, I'd always find out when she was there. That night, however, I came down from my hovel because of the drum noise. The drummers from the broadcasting station had a date with Rita and some members of the Los Dandy *comparsa.* They put on a blasting rumba rumble. The police went after the drums instead of going after the gunshots. Two patrol cars, one from Galiano Street and the other from Lagunas, surrounded the café at around two in the morning. The police officers got out and caused terrible chaos with the oarlock in their hands. They took the drums away from the *rumberos* and handcuffed them. They took them one by one to the patrol car. They were off to the precinct on Zulueta and Dragones. "Let them pay first!" shouted the *guajiro* who had waited on them.

"I'll pay," said Rita Montaner.

She took out some bills, threw them on the little marble table, and with the same attitude she called over the police officer.

"Listen, where do you think you're taking those citizens?"

"They're all going to the station right now. This is not the time of night to create a scandal in a respectable city."

Rita, in a way that was all her own, immediately snapped back at him, "Look, you should be ashamed of yourself, a black man, taking those people in for singing."

"I'm just doing my duty, *Señora,*" the police officer answered her.

"Well then, take me away, too."

And without blinking an eye she got right in the passenger side, front seat of the patrol car that was parked on Galiano. Mamita was right behind her screaming and backing everything Rita said and did.

"Both of you, get in the back," she said to her husband and her friend. "Move!"

The police officer talked to the rest of the squad. They decided to call the district lieutenant.

"Look, Rita, this doesn't involve you. It's not our problem, it's theirs."

"And mine," Rita said to him. "I paid their bills because they were my guests. And in case you didn't know, I was the one who was singing."

"Get out, Rita. Please."

But Rita stayed seated there next to the driver. A few minutes later the lieutenant showed up to mediate between Rita and the officers on duty. She was convinced that if they took her it'd be a scandal. So Rita made the lieutenant send the two patrol cars to the front of the police station. The scandal broke the next day. She sided with the musicians. She wanted to be in their shoes. Finally they let them go. The plan backfired on them. They stayed away from the café on Galiano and Lagunas for months.

Miguelito and Rita got along very well. Every time she'd see him, she'd say to him, "*Chico,* study to be a dentist. You're a fine black man."

It'd bother him because he wanted to be an artist no matter what, but she wouldn't apologize. If you didn't have what it took, she'd rub it in your face. She told it like it was. One day Miguelito told me that Rita once went to fill out some form at the Asociación de Artistas and the guy behind the desk, a real dummy, asked for her age, race, and a bunch of other stuff. Asking a middle-aged mulatta those questions was offensive back then. When he got to the one about race, Rita answered "white" to shut him up.

And he looked at her and like an imbecile whispered, "Rita, I think that . . ."

And she responded with that stabbing wit, "Really? Well, I also think that you're a faggot and I've never told you that."

Miguelito Cuesta managed to get together a good-sized neighborhood claque. It was an impromptu claque made up of friends and others from the Colón neighborhood. He didn't give them a penny. The claques always got something. They'd come as a group, although there were loners who'd make a tremendous fuss. One was like having twenty. Miguelito had everything. However, he never won a competition. Lots of praise, lots of smiles, a sample of Kresto or a pair of Casino socks, but after that, nothing else.

I admired him a lot because he was persistent and impulsive. He was determined to be a singer and, in a way, he did achieve it. When he saw, because he wasn't blind, that he didn't have what it took to be on a big broadcasting station, he went for the charities and hospitals. That's where he got his start, performing for the sick and for veterans. He also got a lot of work with the Association for the Blind and at the tributes to the retired artists from the Alhambra Theatre, the Molino Rojo, and the comedy shows from the beginning of the century. He was a stray bullet. Sometimes days would go by and not even his woman knew where he was. Then he'd appear with a bottle of Matusalem Rum and some money because he'd gone to the Parrandas de Bejucal or to a dance competition in Güines.

"The artist has arrived," his woman would say.

And he would say looking at her with evil eyes, "The Cuban artist!"

I didn't want that kind of life. To tell the truth, I never really liked it. I did what I did so I wouldn't starve to death. I wanted to be a normal person.

Amor y orgullo and *Alma rebelde* were the listeners' favorites. The first was a story about two people who were haunted by selfishness. Emerlina couldn't miss them. She'd spend the entire day with her ear glued to the radio. *Amor y orgullo* was sponsored by Crusellas & Company. CMQ transmitted it. CMQ was RHC's main competitor. The broadcaster would say, "People tormented by the hate of someone who couldn't bear the happiness of their requited love; not until the passion of caring and the relief of the most tattered pain sanctified their bliss." Women would start crying before the show even started. They'd burn the clothes they were ironing. They wouldn't pay attention to their children, their husbands, no one, nothing. Every day I'd warn her, "Don't let what happened to Venancio Prado happen to you."

But it was like talking to a wall. The soap operas of those years were a drug. The only thing my girl would do is come home from work and put on the radio. After two hours, she'd have a splitting headache. Cuba would come upstairs with crushed ice and put it on her forehead and give her lemon water with bee's honey and a Cafiaspirina. She got some very odd migraines that she never got rid of. And she'd raise her voice at me, practically scream at me. She, the woman who never fought with me before. She started to get jealous about everything. She'd repeat the entire soap operas on the radio to me. She was driving me crazy!

"You're cheating on me, Julián. I know it."

I'd go and do my thing when I felt like it, but I never really cheated on her. If you fall hard for another woman, it's cheating; but I loved Emerlina very much. It was painful to see her suffer, making up things that weren't true just because of the radio shows. The poor women would be sick by the time the show was over.

Eva la Libanesa came to tell me about the death of Isaac the shoemaker. He had a heart attack in his own shoe shop while working and collapsed on the floor. When he got to the Casa de Socorros, the emergency hospital, he was still breathing. They gave him an insulin injection thinking that he had a diabetic coma and they killed him. He also had given me a hand. The last thing I did for him was go to his funeral.

I went to look for Miguelito and Ñico so that they'd go with me. But Miguelito came up with one of his typical excuses, "Julián, I'm not even going to my own wake because," and he did have a point, "the dead, in a nutshell, can't see anymore. The living are the ones who suffer. If you think about it, wakes are like bad movies. They last too long. You know what's going to happen at the end. The dead person is the only one who's ready for a party that day with his jacket and tie on." Ñico and I went because the Polish man had been another benefactor in Havana.

When I got home, Emerlina was awake and her skin color looked really bad. She couldn't make it to La Champagne that day. I took her to the emergency room in a taxi because one side of her body was half-paralyzed. She really scared me. Emerlina was a very young woman, but she looked bad. When we got to the hospital it was the last straw. You saw everything in the emergency care centers. You couldn't go to the hospitals. After waiting several hours, they gave her an injection, some pills, and sent us home.

Emerlina woke up with aches and pains and couldn't stand up straight. I went to see the old lady Matilde to tell her Emerlina wouldn't be there; and a few days later, while sewing little nets, she fainted. Matilde brought her to the doctor. I already noticed her getting really weak. It was like you were dealing with a toy doll instead of a person. But she continued going to La Champagne until one day when I discovered some blue spots on the palms of her hands. I took her to the scale at the hospital and she'd lost about thirty pounds. I went to see Matilde and she told me, "I'm very sorry, Julián, but I have to replace her."

The world was closing in on me. I was Emerlina's only family. And in a moment like that, it's necessary to have a relative around, but nothing happened. Her aunt didn't even offer to help out. I had to take care of her myself. I asked Méndez for some help because my salary wasn't even enough for the medicine. Matilde's doctor charged for the analysis and the x-rays. And even though she helped me, my pride was greater than my needs. Emerlina went from bad to worse. The spots spread to her fingernails. Miguelito and Ñico called me to task. "Look, Julián, if you don't admit that woman, she'll die on you."

The doctors didn't know what was wrong with Emerlina. Nothing showed up on the x-rays. But the blood test did show that she lost an enormous amount of red blood cells. I went around looking for Amado Trinidad until I found him. He came in through the back door. Since he was a benefactor, some people would say that the poor would gather around his front door to ask him for favors. I called him. I was desperate. I begged him, "Please get me a bed in a hospital. Please."

"What happened to you?"

"My girl is dying on me, Amado."

"Leave this to me," he answered firmly.

He asked for my home address and promised me that an ambulance from the Reina Mercedes Hospital was going to come get her. But like six or seven days went by and Emerlina was getting weaker by the minute. It was more difficult to get a bed in a hospital than to hit the lottery. That's why I turned to him. In the meantime, Miguelito brought just about every *espiritista* in Havana to my house. They did everything to Emerlina. They said she had the spirit of a suicide victim in her and that they were going to get it out. They rubbed ointments and herbs on her. And for what? Her skin was getting more and more blue every day. She looked like a corpse.

When the ambulance finally showed up, Emerlina was a bag of bones. It was an ambulance from the Casa de Socorros. Ñico got it through a doctor, Orlando Yduante, who was a member of the Partido Ortodoxo. Amado Trinidad and I never saw each other again. The entire *solar* came out to see what was going on. Everyone there loved us because we thought that what went on in your house was your own business. We weren't nosy. When Emerlina was really bad, Cuba would come upstairs every day with some camphor stones so her sickness wouldn't spread. I'd give her yeast pills and boiled eggs, but she was losing her appetite more and more every day. She looked like a cadaver in the ambulance bed. Her head was shaking as if her neck could no longer hold it. Cuba went with her for the ride. When she got back she told me, "Cold water was the only thing she wanted."

I don't really give to collection boxes for charities like the Anti-Cancer League. I think people believe everything. But I gave money once in a while because I felt like I knew what it was to die from that illness. The doctors explained to me that Emerlina had an irregular heartbeat, her blood wasn't receiving oxygen, and that's why she got so blue. That explains the spots on her skin and the lack of shine in her eyes.

When we buried her and I was all alone, I felt like the only person in the world. I felt like it was the biggest tragedy. I went back to my room on Blanco and Virtudes with Cuba and her husband. I've always been very strong. And I didn't shed one single tear at the funeral or in the cemetery. But when I saw the Phillips radio on the nightstand, I had to cover my mouth with a handkerchief.

Now that I was alone in the world I didn't give a damn about anything. I lost control of everything. After a few months I had a girl move in with me. She was one of Ñico's friends and she'd gone out with me several times. She wasn't a bad woman, but she had a sister who was a big hussy. She made her home life impossible. So I said to her, "Move in with me, baby."

But there was no falling in love, no lust. I just did it for the company. She and Miguelito got along very well and the people in the *cuartería* didn't throw it in my face. My sister and brother sent me their condolences, but I didn't thank them. I distanced myself a lot from my family because Emerlina was my everything. Sometimes I'd stare at the wall with the radio on and my woman would ask me, "What's wrong, Julián?"

Nothing. Nothing was wrong.

An overbearing, politically driven woman from the Pueblo Nuevo neighborhood was the one who told on me. She was a big fan of Mexican music. When Tito Guizar came to Havana, she burned him on the hand with a cigarette so he'd look at her. She was locked up. And she wasn't allowed into RHC because she'd bring claques of twenty and thirty people. She promised to pay and then she wouldn't give them a penny. The claque really went after her at the station door and formed a terrible racket. Then Amado Trinidad said, "The racket's over. Lock her up."

And they took her away because he was just as powerful as a police officer.

A few days later she got out on bail and stood guard waiting for Amado. She managed to talk to him. She must've given him tremendous lip or known something about him because he let her come back to the programs. How did she do it? I don't know. But she had some shady deal with the boss. It became some sort of give and take. She'd have her helpers let him know everything she saw at the door.

I got a bad feeling about Rebeca. I didn't like how she acted like a man. She was a troublemaker. If she hadn't had permission from the owner, I wouldn't have let her in ever again. I got the chills when I found out that Rebeca went to Amado Trinidad's Santa Barbara parties at his *finca* every year on December 4th and that she was close with his wife, Flor Angel Cañizo. But it was too late. Rebeca told him something, and one day, the manager called me in and said to me, "I'm very sorry, but we have to let you go."

Without any explanation they got rid of me. I shot right out of there. I started to walk home and heard someone calling me from the bar on the corner. Hortensia, the owner's wife, talked to me in her own way. She knew what she was talking about.

"You lasted there longer than you should have, Son."

She bayed for Amado Trinidad's blood. When he hanged himself on his *finca* she was the first to scream at the top of her lungs that he'd taken his own life because he had a bad conscience and made promises to people and never followed through. Amado got wind that I blamed him for Emerlina's death and tried to get me out of his way. It was as clear as day.

"Thank you, Hortensia."

And I kept walking as if I'd been waiting a while for what had just happened. I walked into the patio of my house, went up the stairs, and said to Amparo, "Now the party's really over, Girl."

Since she wasn't like Emerlina she looked at me with a scared face. I explained the situation to her. I tried to make her understand me, but it was useless. She said to me, "I don't clean for just anyone. I want a man who looks after me."

I'd have hit her, but I controlled myself. I wasn't going to do myself in for a woman who was just a fling. The walls came crashing down on me. It was the pits. And, oh, how I'd dreamed about Havana! Thinking things could only get better! But, when it rains, it pours. Amparo went to buy the newspaper. In the classifieds there was an ad for a driver, and I didn't know how to drive. On top of that they wanted a Spaniard and letters of recommendation. I couldn't be a cook either. They wanted a Chinese man and I was *capirro*, a light-skinned mulatto, and I didn't know how to cook. The benefactors were in desperate situations. And Ñico wasn't going to recommend me again. If there had been a hole in the ground to suck me in, I would've been happy! I threw a bucket of cold water on my head and, without saying a word to Amparo, I left with no particular place to go.

"Julián, Julián!" she started to yell, but I didn't look back. I thought to myself, "For someone who likes Havana so much and has so much patriotism, I shouldn't be having such a hard time." Those who were born bad lived like Carmelina. They received monthly checks directly from the President of the Republic. All because they were bullying beggars and the government protected them. El Colorado, a professional *botellero*, had four hundred positions in his wallet to hand out. Policarpo Soler, the worst of the gangsters, the most feared, had six hundred. And the others, of less caliber but in the same type of business, carried between forty and sixty positions for their toadies. Their money came from the Palacio Presidencial with the letterhead "President of the Republic, Personal Matter." Carlos Prío bought peace and guaranteed his seat in office. And he received shoot-outs and assassination attempts. Prío's government even made the blood of serious politicians boil. I'm talking about the ones who at least had a clean history in their province.

The first time I heard anyone talk about Fidel Castro was when I first got to New York. Fidel accused him of being a gang member and of having risen to power protected by all that shrapnel. And he complained to the Court of Audit about Prío's crimes and embezzlements. "Prío pays for the guns that kill. Prío pays for the cars used to kill. Prío pays the men who kill." That's how the news about the appeal spread throughout the newspapers. It reached us here in New York right away and Fidel Castro started to gain sympathizers among us Cubans.

Like a crazy man without knowing where to go, I sat on a bench on the Prado and asked a young shoeshine boy to clean my shoes. I bought a *crocante de maní*, a hard piece of peanut candy, said hello to a few people I knew, and when I got back home I didn't have a penny in my pocket. I walked into that patio filled with wash pans and clotheslines without even saying good afternoon. I went up to my room and found Amparo sprawled out on the bed and crying as if the whole world were against her.

When you most need your friends they're nowhere to be found. Miguelito didn't go by the broadcasting station until a week after they'd gotten rid of me. He went to look for me on the night shift and when he asked for me the new doorman went crazy.

"Where the heck were you?" I asked him when he showed up at my place.

"Trying to make some peanuts, My Man, trying to make some peanuts."

He knew that Rebeca had sold herself to Amado Trinidad and he said I was right about everything. He went to buy a bottle of rum and between the three of us we drank it in two hours.

"What do you think, Miguelito?

"It looks bad, Julián. It looks bad."

I thought about Méndez, the old lady Matilde, and Eva. I crossed off the first two names and went to see Eva. I paid her the rent religiously. And I was the only man who lived there permanently. In some ways that was good for her. She didn't have to worry about Amparo. She was very good to me when the thing happened with Emerlina. She slipped a little something extra in my hand and sent a spray of white flowers. Eva's business wasn't the rooms or the hovel on Blanco. It was gambling and being friends with the neighborhood policemen. She'd toss the *bolita* a couple of times a day, but there wasn't much in the pot. And that wasn't going to make her rich. That's why she'd do other things. She knew the *pipisigallo*: doctors who performed abortions, notaries, judges, and most importantly Carabelita. Carabelita was the best-looking policeman and had the biggest head in the entire Colón neighborhood. They even knew about him in Luyanó because on the corner of Toyo he raided marijuana sellers and pimps. He was corrupt. He'd lock people up so he could then blackmail them. He'd grab a *guayabito*, a neighborhood pimp, and say to him, "Give me fifty pesos and I'll let you go right here. That's your bail. And take off that wristwatch, it's stolen."

That's how that thief would rake it in. People were terrified of him. He respected Eva because she had hair on her chest. She'd put a black tobacco cigarette in the corner of her mouth and threaten his life."

"Yes, I will kill you, you son of a bitch."

And he'd get frightened like a good little mouse. He was scared of women. And he'd known Eva ever since she got to the neighborhood. They say she was very beautiful with big black gypsy eyes. Since she didn't speak Spanish she'd put a sign hanging around her neck and go around selling threads, fabrics, and cosmetics from her uncle's discount store. He died in a brawl on Caballería pier. Her sign would list the prices and what she was selling. She became popular in Havana because she was selling stuff very cheap for the time. Later, she kept the discount store and expanded the business.

"Eva, I got fired from the broadcasting station. I'm here to ask you for help."

And at the same time I paid her two months rent up front so that she knew I was for real.

"I'll be in touch. Don't worry," she said to me, without taking the cigarette out of her mouth.

Amparo started cleaning for other people behind my back. She cleaned for the women who lived in the *solar*, and even for Eva. That's how we survived. Even though I've never really been very fond of having my woman work, I let my arm be twisted . . .

Amparo and Eva got along very well. If there was something good about my woman, it was that she worked hard around the house. She was a little off her rocker, as they say, but she did work hard around the house. Her mother died when she was just a girl. And her stepfather had done horrible things to her. He tried to rape Amparo several times, when she was a little girl. He'd touch her at night. He'd watch her like a hawk. He cut her hair with a garden scissor so she couldn't put it up. When she turned fourteen, she moved in with her sister. She was her servant until I could get her out of there, thanks to Miguelito. The sister lived in a real seedy joint full of drugs and prostitution, but Amparo, like a swan, didn't get her wings dirty in the mud. The first day I slept with her I noticed some marks on her back and neck. They were scars that her sister had given her when she wouldn't do her a favor or she'd criticize her behavior with some married man. Eva listened to her stories and made her feel better. Amparo always said the same thing over and over, "Oh, Eva, I want to walk out of my house and go to the Iglesia de Monserrate with a veil, a crown, and a dress with a train! I want to have children and a mahogany bedroom set with a mirror and a dresser. And most of all get married. Yes! Get married! If Julián would settle down, we'd be happy!"

I'd hear everything and say to myself, "I won't marry you because you're a very greedy woman." And Eva, what was she going to do?

She agreed with her and then did her own thing. She also had a lot of stories, the poor thing. They say she was sent to Cuba as a very young girl and that her uncle, who was more than forty years older, wanted to screw her. She'd always say, "I came over on the ship *Marqués de Comillas* with braids to my waist and shooing away *gallegos* like flies."

Amparo and I were done. I didn't ask her to get out of my house because I felt bad. Then Miguelito's *espiritista* friends started telling me, "Look, Julián, you don't believe in anything, but I'm going to tell you something. Do you know what a bird of bad omen is? Well that woman is a bird of bad omen and she's casting spells on you under your own roof. Have a good look at your clothing, your pillow, the soles of your shoes, and you'll see how many things there are scattered around there."

Things did start to get better when I stopped seeing her, that's for sure. Amparo wanted to marry a businessman or someone in the military. And I was starving to death with a pair of two-toned shoes to show off. The problem didn't ask for permission, it said, "Here I am!" And as if that wasn't enough, Miguelito and I were sent to jail for trying to sell lottery tickets without paying for a license. Everything happens for a reason: jail was a fucked-up experience, but I learned a lot.

I was totally broke and completely desperate for Amparo's compassion. So Miguelito and I decided to sell tickets from the Plaza del Polvorín.

"You can't make a living as an artist, Julián. I'm not going to get on a bus from the Cooperativa de Omnibus Aliados Company and collect fares. And there are no more contracts."

Miguelito gave himself away as a leftist sympathizer when Prío's people closed down the newspaper *Hoy*. They did away with it by saying that it was to clean up. Miguelito along with other old artists from Mil Diez radio station protested publicly.

We'd buy the tickets for eighteen cents in the plaza and resell them to some Mr. Mosquera who owned a kiosk on the corner of Toyo. We'd get out very early when Havana was a ghost town. We'd hang off the bus like fleas so we wouldn't have to pay. If the driver caught us, we'd jump off and catch the next one. To tell the truth, we turned into wasps. That's how we avoided the police for a few weeks.

I'd get home with some pennies in my pocket, dead tired. And when I'd go to throw a pail of water over my head, the same thing again and again, "This isn't life, this is no way to live."

I took a plaster figure of a saint from on top of the cupboard and threw it on the floor.

"You're going to get yourself locked up, damn it," she screamed at me.

I threw a bucket of water on my head and walked out of the bathroom naked to pick up the little pieces of plaster. I put them in a cardboard box and threw them in the garbage can.

I don't know if it was a curse, but a few days later a police officer, last name Aspirina, asked us for our license. Miguelito had it out with him. While they were yelling at each other, I saw that when the police officer took out his stick to hit Miguelito on the legs, he had started to run up Vives Street. When I got to a small park behind a church, Aspirina and Miguelito were wrestling each other. I got involved in the fight. I gave him a hefty punch and threw him on a bench. We started to run but people yelled, "Stop them, stop them!" The patrol car caught us on the corner of Tallapiedra Power Plant. The world was closing in on me.

Prison was no joke. If in the countryside you go hungry, in prison your stomach sticks to your spine. The first week behinds bars was the worst. The hours dragged on and the days seemed like they'd never end. Sometimes a ray of light would shine through the window and it was as if a blessing were falling from the sky. But when they'd serve that watery, stinky garlic soup, and close the iron door, I felt as if they were taking a hammer to my head because the noise really messed with me. If they brought the food to the crazies at Mazorra hospital in a garbage truck, it wasn't a surprise that the guy who stunk the most like goat in the whole jail passed out the food there. Even though I knew that we weren't going to be there for a long time, the fact that I couldn't get out, or that my hands and feet were tied up, made me understand that the only thing that man really has is his freedom. That's what he needs to worry about most.

Night in jail was much more terrible than day. During the day, between the stories, the rumbas on the patio, the meals, time more or less went by. But nighttime was scary. If you weren't a tough guy, you'd run the risk that any old pervert would want to come and rape you. I saw gigantic ones, thugs, wake up little young boys and rip open their faces with their sharp pinky fingernail. The most violent things happened under the electric light bulbs in the cells. Since they stayed on until five in the morning, night in prison was completely bright.

During the trial Aspirina said whatever he felt like, "The white guy had a knife on him. And the black guy has the record of a professional thief at the police station."

No proof, nothing. They didn't even ask for it. Just like that, on a whim. Justice was done and they'd put you in jail for any silly thing. They gave us a year of jail time, but it was reduced to three months. The prosecutor realized the abuse that was taking place and lowered the sanction. We went to trial dressed in the blue uniform. For a hardworking man like myself, to see myself bald like a dasheen plant, with that mixed cloth suit on was an embarrassment.

"I prayed to Ochosi for you," Amparo told me on the landing that went to the courtroom.

Ñico and Eva went to the trial, but they couldn't do anything. Ñico with his good attitude and compassionate glance said to me, "You'll get over this, Julián. It's part of the job."

And Eva looked at our faces and with tremendous confidence said to us, "I'll bring you Príncipe cigarettes. I'm going to talk to Dr. Peñante and Carabelita."

Exactly a month later Eva, Amparo, and Miguelito's woman

came to visit. They brought us cigarettes and guava treats. A visit from your allies at a place like that is like hitting the lottery. Amparo blurted out, "You look like a ghost." And it was true because when I got out, on the scale in the main room upstairs, I weighed thirty-two pounds less. Eva assured me that she had a job for me. Amparo looked at me and as if it were like asking for a glass of water, right there between the bars, she begged me, "Julián, when you get out buy me a television."

God knows why I didn't tell her to go to hell. I got the chills from head to toe. A television was the thing to have, it just came out. But asking me for a television in those circumstances was a long shot. "How am I going to get rid of this woman?" was the only thing that came to mind at that moment.

"You'll be *ñáñigos* by the time you get out of here," Eva la Libanesa said to us with a cigarette in her mouth.

The *ñáñigos*, members of the Afro-Cuban secret society called Abakua, really didn't do anything bad in prison, nor did they eat anybody or take anyone's heart out. Politicians spread all that nonsense to make them look bad. In jail you had to watch out for the thugs not to be messed with. They had more of a life inside than outside of jail. And when you least expected it, they'd dig a ditch in your back with a sharpened spoon, to get you to give them your cigarette. And watch out if you took their turn in the bathroom or at the barber.

"Listen you, you scoundrel, that's my shower. Get out."

If you got wise with them that was it. The best thing to do was to get out all wet, and then wait as long as he wanted you to in order to go back in. They were always first: with the plate of food, you had to give it to them; at the barber, I already said what would happen; and even in line for recess on the patio. They'd break the light bulbs with their nails and then boast that they'd done it with one spit. And they knew a wrestling move, a secret move, they used to grab someone from behind and hurt him. That's why when the light bulbs started to break, the people in the cell would shake and pretend to be asleep.

You see everything in jail. You also see crazy men. They're usually there because of a mistake. Or because they took out their prick in a park or touched a young lady's behind. There are those who think they are Napoleon. Or those who dream about mermaids, such as Margarito, a black baker who claimed to have slept with a woman who was a fish from the waist down. Listen and keep quiet. Jail makes you think about thousands of things. And there are even those who get used to being there and when the door is opened, they start to scream and don't want to leave. You see everything and get to know the other part of life: the savage man.

Escaparate was one of the bosses in the lion's den. He was a prisoner sentenced for many years, probably for murder. He got revenge on the others by insulting them. He'd get to the lion's den, the inmates' cell, and treat the people like cattle. In the lion's den there were about three hundred and fifty prisoners. Miguelito and I were among them. Escaparate would shout, "Stupid!" at anyone for no reason. He'd do it just because he ruled that place. He was a big mulatto as his nickname suggested. He was even scared of himself. As a young boy he took out his teeth and his molars because he said, "Toothaches are for sissies." When he had to serve breakfast or lunch, it was a headache. He'd pretend that the *café con leche* would spill or give you a day-old piece of bread. We went from garlic soup to flour. For breakfast he was the *Malquerida* and for lunch *Grano de oro*. Escaparate got off clanging the tin plates and shouting out "rice with calamari" or "lobster enchilada"; that bastard was a sadist. I didn't see it, but Miguelito and Gabriel Piña, a musician in a band whose nickname was *Pan de Gloria*, saw how Escaparate sexually abused two young boys by the cell number one bathroom. He'd threaten them by cutting them or offering them more food and more favors. And he'd do it all right under your nose.

At six in the evening, they'd bring out the flag. A guard would come and shout: "Attention!" All the prisoners would line up and salute the flag. At nine everyone had to be quiet. You'd sink in a total loss of life. That's when prisoners realize they're locked up. You couldn't even talk softly because the beasts would make you shut up. Or they'd throw buckets of cold water through the windows. Anyway, it was all over.

This is a very funny story but it's kind of gross. One night Miguelito had diarrhea. The only thing he could do was to ask the corporal for permission to go to the toilet. But, the corporal was either drunk or there was someone using the toilet. It was certain that Miguelito got tired of screaming. The corporal finally answered him, "Come on," but it was too late. And the only thing that Miguelito could do was shout "I already went!" The entire lion's den looked. They sent Escaparate to clean up the mess with wet rice sacks. The stench lasted for several days because in jail there's no *creolina* or disinfectants. Only water and jute sacks instead of blankets.

That's why the cell was never clean and there were so many epidemics in there. During my time there, two epidemics broke out. One was typhus, from which I was saved because I had it as a kid. The another was amebic dysentery. Typhus spread like a bad spell since there was only one toilet. The cells and dungeons were covered with sulfur and they'd wash us prisoners with alcohol from the bodega every day. Since you don't have rights in jail, but rather duties, they made the older prisoners rub the rest of us with alcohol.

Miguelito and I made an agreement with one of them. We saved alcohol in the empty condensed milk cans to make *mofuco*. Jail *mofuco* isn't like the one you find on the street. The jail one is made by mixing alcohol with water and adding a little bit of sugar. It was a relief to have a sip of something hot during the winter months. *Mofuco* was the prisoner's cocktail in Cuba. It tasted divine because it was forbidden.

Another sickness affected the skin. Almost everyone had a rash on their skin because of the liver parasite. At first, the doctors didn't know what in the world it was and they started to give out pills and rub the skin. But the rashes went from bad to worse. I completely lost my appetite and almost my will to live. They saw me in that state and sent me straight to the infirmary. That's the room where the people with no hope of recovering went. I think it was called the Hidalgo Room. I saw atrocities there. Three or four prisoners died per day right next to me. Especially those who didn't want to try to eat. Seeing that made me feel like eating and I even got to eat bread with water. That diet lifted my spirits a little. I asked the nurse to send me to Miami, that's the room where you could survive. The prisoners called it Miami because it was better there, like at a seaside resort. And they didn't force you to line up or salute the flag. I got better in Miami while the others were dying. Luckily the vaccines worked on me. I got eighteen vaccines in the radial vein. The treatment was worse than the disease. I spent almost the entire time in the infirmary. That helped my pain a lot. I couldn't have visitors there, but through Miguelito I found out that Amparo and Eva had come by twice to bring me guava paste and condensed milk and to see how I was doing.

Gorrita was next to me in the infirmary. He was a strange guy. Also of Lebanese descent. He was dying and didn't say a word to anybody. When he came to trust me, because we'd pass the bread to each other, he told me that tuberculosis totally wiped him out. They had sent him there to get better but he wanted to return to Presidio Modelo, another prison, on Isla de Pinos. If a prisoner broke the rules on that island they'd kill him. And Gorrita said, "I'd rather die from a bullet than from this damn tuberculosis."

And he'd put his head out the window to get some sun and to warm up his chest a bit. But he'd still spend the whole day with a white rag on his mouth and coughing. He was already on the other side. Before dying, he told me his life story. I felt like his confessor. He'd been a bandit through and through, a boss of groups of women all over the island of Cuba. He organized gangs of *borregos*, women dressed in long gypsy-like clothing with pockets and lining in their skirts so that they could rob by holding out their hands.

He organized the baby-sitters gang. It was made up of kids

who were anywhere from seven to eleven or twelve years old. Two adults would start to fight and the kids would take advantage of the situation by pickpocketing them and stealing their wristwatches. Sometimes they'd go around with backpacks or bags. Gorrita was thrown out of Mexico because he organized the guitar steal in Lagunillas. It was a perfect con to get tokens and money. He threw off the police because no one suspected that a guy with a guitar in his hand was going to be an undercover thief.

Garrito vegetated on the Isla de Pinos because his ambition made him go crazy. He tried to rob a *gallego* butcher in Placetas. He went in the butcher shop and thought, because he was Gorrita, "This *gallego* will get on his knees." But the feisty *gallego* stood in front of the cash register and stayed there until Gorrita, blinded by his desire for more, put the knife used to cut bones through him.

The murderer was caught the next day. Gorrita promised some of the town gamblers big commissions for future robberies with the money from the register. They gave him away because everyone loved the *gallego* in Placetas and Gorrita was just another scoundrel. That's it. His plan backfired on him.

Miguelito and I didn't receive any punishments in prison. But between a dungeon punishment and death, I'd have preferred death. In jail, they'd do searches every day to find out who had money, who made knives, or who carried scissors. They gave a tough punishment to whomever they caught. It was either the dungeon or the *baile del tiburón*. The dungeon was the last card in the deck. They'd throw the prisoner completely naked in a small cell and sometimes forget to feed him. They'd throw buckets of water on him to bathe him as if he were a caged animal. If you survived that punishment, you came out of there with your morale up and elephant skin.

The *baile del tiburón*, or the shark dance, was a way of torturing the prisoner. They'd lay the prisoner down on a thick gravel floor, and throw buckets of water on him. Then lash him with a whip until you could see the wounds. Then they'd clean them, if you want to call it that, with salt and vinegar. The prisoner had to swim like a shark on the gravel and in the puddle of water. They discovered a forty-cent coin on a Catalan hidden in a bar of yellow soap, and they gave him the shark until the Catalan passed out on the gravel.

Life on the street was revolting, but in jail it was hell. I saw the devil in a man's body between those bars. That's why nothing catches me by surprise. When someone tells you with such cold blood that he killed his mother or raped a five-year-old and then offers you a cigarette or makes a toast with his milk can, what are you supposed to think about mankind? Hearing those stories and seeing what I saw, I came to the conclusion that criminals are not born, but made. Jail helped me to understand many things about life in Cuba. That's why here in New York when I see what happens in the Bronx or on the Lower East Side or in Harlem, I blame the government, the ruling class in this country, that only thinks about their stomachs and taking over the world with nuclear arms.

Jail incited me. And when I got out, I said to Miguelito, "Look, my life is going to change."

He already had an idea for us to go around in fruit ships to the ports out there. And that got us thinking. But since it's hard to deny natural urges, on the day we got out I went home around noon or one in the afternoon. I surprised my girl. I picked up some money and went to drink some beers with Miguelito and Ñico at the Puerta de Tierra Bar.

"You guys have really lost your looks."

"Damn it, Ñico. If I told you half of it, you wouldn't believe me."

Miguelito left right away and went to look for his girl. He had lust in his eyes and the itch in his body. He couldn't contain himself.

"I'm good for three, Brother. I'm good for three."

And he went up Monserrate, happy to be on the street. Because freedom is the greatest thing a man has.

When it got dark, I sat with Ñico in Parque Central to listen to the Military Band's open-air concert. I told him emphatically, "I'm going to break up with Amparo."

Ñico gave me good advice to end it peacefully. Also, he told me that Eva had distanced herself from my woman. That gave me the chills from head to toe. Someone who understands things well doesn't need to say much. Eva didn't mess around. She had managed to get me out of Príncipe earlier and had a job ready for me. I went to see her at the variety store and with her hoarse voice she told me about what she had set up for me. I'd be a traveling salesman. The variety store was a cover. The only thing they sold there were cigarettes, tissues and stupid things. The real business came from the *bolita*, that's what kept Eva afloat. And she also got a commission for taking patients to see some Dr. Grillo, the one who did abortions in the Colón neighborhood.

"Be there tomorrow at the crack of dawn."

"Thanks, Eva. You're very good. Now, what do you know about Amparo?"

"You do whatever you feel like, but it seems to me that she's always getting together with a police officer."

I went around the neighborhood right before it got dark. The brothels had a red light bulb above the door. When the bulb was on there was room. When it was off, things were really rocking. For a few months the women hid themselves a little behind the lace curtains. Before that, they'd parade around with little on in the middle of the street and open their legs and sit in the doorway. But the Ministry of Public Health made them go inside. That's why the only way of knowing was the little red light bulb.

I went in there like a bull and chose Perlita, a young peasant girl from Tumas. She'd just gotten there and wasn't even seventeen. When she took all her clothes off and leaned against the closet mirror, I became fixated on her bellybutton, "Boy, what are you looking at?" But I didn't want to tell her the story about the Haitian girl. She got me going anyway.

I was wide awake when I got out of there. I drank a *guarapo* on the Malecón and Escobar Street and went directly home. Amparo tried to beat me to it by saying that I was drunk.

"Get all your stuff. There's nothing to explain."

"Are you crazy? You're ungrateful. With all the sacrifices I made and how I waited for you! Where do I go now?"

"Get all your stuff now, damn it!"

She started to scream at me. I didn't do a thing. Then she called Cuba, who already had her ear to the door and the two of them packed her suitcase. Amparo slept downstairs that night, in Milagros's room—she was a bandit. And the next day she was out of there in a taxi from the newspaper *El Mundo* taxi stand. Cuba knocked on my door with a cup of *café con leche* and bread and butter and said to me, "It's the best thing you could do, Julián. That woman is prison meat and you're too young to ruin your life."

I took all the pictures of saints, the makeup, everything that she left behind and burned it in a garbage can. I thought a lot about Emerlina then, and how she'd died on me from blue baby . . .

Miguelito came in a hurry to tell me that the "Espíritu Santo," a fruit ship from Perú, was anchored at the port. The captain was recruiting seamen.

"Let's do the paperwork and get out of here, Man."

But I talked him out of it because today's adventure could be dangerous tomorrow. I regretted it later on. In the middle of a heavy rainstorm, I went to see Eva's Polish friend. He was a Polish Jew with a glass eye. He hardly spoke Spanish. He got here after fleeing from the Nazis and had the number 002213 on his right arm. It was a blue tattoo given to him in the concentration camp. Michel explained to me in his way the type of work I was going to do. He had inherited from another Jew the representation of Goodyear balloons and El Pavo Real matches in the province of Havana. But he didn't tell me that; a Jew to the end. Since I saw him living in such poor conditions I thought he was a wholesale trader. So I agreed to a set commission for the grosses of balloons and matches. His wife would sew for people and when I'd go to the house on Muralla and Compostela, she'd offer me cake she made. She'd laugh with her mouth full of gold teeth and show me her legs.

"Your feet hard, Julián."

Ana and Michel became our friends, good friends. Miguelito and I would kill our hunger there when things were rough. It was the only house in the entire neighborhood where they didn't eat flour. Eva also gave me some grosses of combs and safety pins, and with that job I covered all the streets of Havana for a few months. If there's a street in Havana that I don't know, you can chop off my hand. I had clients on almost all of them. The years at RHC taught me about public relations and the long walks from my house to the sugarcane field trained me for the new job.

Working makes me honorable. I've never gone around like a bum on the corner or turned into a victim of society to later complain about not wanting to get my hands dirty. Many people do that here.

Miguelito started to sell pieces of sugarcane. What a solution! He'd find them for next to nothing at Mercado Único. That black man and I had a magnet for each other. Sometimes I'd turn a corner with my balloons and matches and bump into him.

"Damn it! What are you doing here?"

Destiny is for *espiritistas* whether it exists or not. But we did find each other, that's for sure. It was always like that. One October 10th I got home late and beat from so much walking. I remember the date because it's the anniversary of the Cry of Yara. And when I get in the hallway, I hear fighting coming from Milagros's room. She was shouting and he was threatening her.

"I'll bite you, you big whore!" a man was saying to her.

And she let out a shrill scream, but no one would peek their head in to see what was going on. So I ran out in the street to look for someone. A police officer, someone to help me. And I see Miguelito on his way to my house.

"What's going on?"

"Someone is going to kill Milagros."

And we raced in there. The guy continued threatening her and we were at the door warning him that we were going to call the police. That's when the other neighbors came out onto the patio and it turned into a huge riot. Everyone wanted to see, but no one would get close to the door. Milagros was barely screaming, but the man kept on about it, "I'll bite you if you don't give me back my money."

In one kick I knocked down the door. The guy took out his knife on me. He put it to my throat. Miguelito threw himself at his legs but he couldn't stop that asshole from cutting me. I still have a mark from the twelve stitches from the wound. I mostly think about it in the winter because that's when it bothers me a little. When it's humid out. Milagros went running out of her room and headed for Blanco Street. None of the women there let her into their room. The guy grabbed her on Consulado Street and beat her in front of everybody. I ran out of there with a towel on my neck and went to the Casa de Socorros where they took care of me. Then there was a trial. I didn't want to show up so that things would then be turned against me. Milagros was in critical condition for about three days. She died of a sudden blood poisoning. She turned purple overnight and her hair fell out.

A few days later Eva told me that Milagros had a daughter named Isabel with that man. For six months he was sending her money for the girl through a friend, another girl in the same line of work. Your own can hurt you more than anyone else. The friend told the guy that Milagros had sent Isabel to Fomento in Las Villas, where her mother was raising her, and that she was using the money for herself. And I was the one, like a retard, who paid for it. As they say in my town, the curse of Júa was cast on me. The guy, already a prisoner, said in the trial, "I don't regret a thing," because he was macho and a loud mouth. And a woman couldn't handle him like that. He might be on the street, or around here doing his thing, because he was still young. So as I was saying, destiny is destiny. And Miguelito is still my best friend in this city, the only one I can trust.

I remember that Havana was very rough back the 50s. And I always had acute earring so that nobody would make up stories about me.

Sometimes we'd get together at Bar Rodríguez on Neptuno and Soledad Streets. Or we'd go to Méndez's billiard hall or the little park at the train station. Everything was banditry and strikes for no reason. No one had faith in the Secretary General of the CTC. A malaria epidemic broke out and wiped out absolutely everything. But I'm strong like a bull and nothing happened to me. It was a very, very bad year.

Eusebio Mujal threw the communists out of the Confederation of Cuba Workers, and the people from the villages were very disappointed. I'd hear about everything because Miguelito's brother was a communist. He'd tell us about this and that and that's how . . . The communists had proposed one shift in the summer. In other words, to work from 8:30 to 12:30. That didn't catch on either. I remember a politician with a big ring and a cigar in his mouth named Eurasio said to the people in the park, "The communists attacked the bull to see the blood spill."

The communists wanted the best for the workers and the bull was already loose. No one wanted Prío. Everyone knew he was a dummy. He let drugs be sold on the corners out in the open. I lived through that in Havana. He signed a bonus for teachers and government employees. But I didn't even see the leftovers. The work I did for Michel paid about twelve or fourteen pesos a week. It was enough to pay for the room but I was never able buy myself a full suit.

CMQ was the only thing that made me happy during that time. It crushed RHC. They installed a seventy-thousand-pound television tower that was over four hundred feet high. I saw the decline of Amado Trinidad. His ruin for being self-seeking and a tyrant. Of course, I had ways of entertaining myself because you must always see the good side of things. I saw some films like *Salón México* and others. I saw Brenda the ballerina and went to the Mulatas de Fuego shows. Since I had friends who worked at CMQ, I'd go there at night without paying a dime and see *Fiesta con Bacardí*. That was a good program in the middle of all the soap operas and nonsense.

Lots of disorder, *revolú,* as the Boricuas say here, broke out when La Platanito got to Cuba. The press found out right away that she wasn't allowed to stay in a hotel because she was black. It was a fat scandal. I also saw her on *De Fiesta con Bacardí.* The Teatro Fausto was very expensive. I couldn't afford it. Miguelito went to meet Bobby Capó and said to him in front of me, "I'm a singer and want to go to Puerto Rico."

And Bobby answered him, "Man, the artists in Puerto Rico are crazy about coming to Cuba."

Latin American artists always had a large following in Cuba. They all wanted to make a stop there. They called Bobby Capó "El Astro del Bolero." The women wanted to eat him alive right there in the street. And when I say I alive, I mean it! Boricuas were the thing in Havana during those years. Two of them tried to kill President Truman in Washington. They tried to sneak into the president's residence at gunpoint. One of them was killed. One of Truman's personal bodyguards was also killed. And Truman went to the funeral. Well, it was the only thing that people talked about in Havana. Even Albizu Campos was imprisoned because he was accused of complicity in the attack on La Fortaleza in San Juan. He surrendered at gunpoint because they teargassed his house. He looked unkempt in the photos and very out of it. I learned about Pedro Albizu Campos here in New York. A patriotic man, not a crazy man like they were saying.

Life in the capital polished me up. I worked at it, of course; after all, that had always been my goal. As I said before, oxen are the rough ones. It polished me and opened my eyes. Men from the countryside are crafty and think twice about things but they don't have that boldness of the city. That zest for going out without a plan and letting yourself get swept away by the current. That's real freedom. That's why in spite of everything I liked Havana and it never occurred to me to look back.

My last job was the one with the balloons and matches. I'm going to tell a little about it. Gaspar was showy. He made a living at the expense of others, from things he didn't directly work on. He had two or three carts of crushed-ice drinks on Regla Street. He also wanted to monopolize matches sales in Havana. He was always drunk, but even so he had a very clear head for business. When he'd go to say your name, he'd rattle off, "It's nice to meet you, my name is Melchor, Gaspar, and Baltasar because I was born on January 6th, but everyone knows me as Gaspar Pita."

Gaspar was what in Oriente is called a *mulato remendado*, a way of calling mulattos with green eyes. And those mulattos didn't mean well. People didn't trust them. Ever since the first time I saw him, I said to myself, "What bad luck, damn it! I got stuck with another one of these bastards." And that's the way it was. I got in a bad mood. He liked to tease people without taking into consideration that not everyone is the same. When we'd run into each other at Ana and Michel's house, he'd look at me like he wanted to eat me alive. It bothered him that I sold matches. He'd speak softly with the Polish man and later always ask me the same thing, "So, how's it going?"

"Not too bad considering the weather," I'd reply.

He'd get in my way. I'd get to a variety store or a food store and the owners would say to me, "Your partner was already here."

"He's not my partner. No, not at all. He's a smart aleck."

He'd go there himself or send one of his buddies so that when I'd get there it'd already be too late. I warned my clients about what was going on and some of them listened to me. Gaspar on his bicycle had no problem getting there before me. But since he had a big mouth, some of the *gallegos* who owned bodegas didn't like him. They waited for me. That saved me a little because Gaspar was, in proper English, bad news. Michel wanted to sell and did nothing to avoid a fight. One afternoon we ran into each other at the end of the Lisa Bridge. Gaspar had covered almost all of Marianao and there wasn't even one kiosk left for me to visit.

"Look, Gaspar, now you've really fucked me up."

"No one owns the street, Brother," and he jumped back on his bike. It was like seeing the devil before me. I grabbed a pipe and ran after him hitting him all over the place. On his legs, on his head, on his back. I saw him fall on the pavement in pain, gasping. I got the heck out of there. I took Route 22, something I'd never done because I usually walked from La Lisa to Havana every day. I said to myself, "Now the world can come to an end. And if I killed him, he deserved it."

But it wasn't like that. Gaspar had seven lives like cats do. He ran to complain to Michel. He got a gang of bandits after me because he was a coward. He got scared of me, he ran away from me. The gang waited for me at my house twice. The first time they verbally threatened me. And the second they gave me a beating. I fell to the ground like a sack on the curb. But the coward got away. I told Michel, "If I run into Gaspar Pita, I'll kill him." And believe it or not, he stayed out of my area. He'd go do business at night and sell stuff in Regla and Guanabacoa so that he wouldn't run into me.

If things got bad for me, they were worse for Miguelito. I got the chills seeing him sell pieces of sugarcane on the corners when he was into singing and tap dancing.

"Julián, things are really bad. I went to the docks. I spoke to Emiliano, to the *Curro*, the black dandy, to everyone, there's not even anything as a dockworker there."

When we saw each other, we'd always talk about the same thing or have a coffee at his house. There his girl with her *espiritismo* stuff would tell us that her guide told her we had a dark spirit and it was necessary to get rid of it with cleansing baths, herbs and white doves.

I don't know if it had to do with those spirits or what, but the balloons and matches thing failed overnight. The balloons didn't work out because the Spanish bodega owners started to join co-ops at the Lonja del Comercio and they'd buy and sell among themselves. I even started to hate the Spanish female musicians. And I'd always really liked the pasodoble. Something similar happened with the matches. They started to sell for three fifty a gross through a trust association with the Swedes. So the wholesaler didn't need agents because they bought them from him directly and by mail. So I was back on the street once again. I didn't even make enough with the thing with Eva to buy gum.

I fell in a hole again. I started to look for work as a builder, a waiter, even as a servant in a private home. But since I knew how to read and write, they'd tell me, "Go look for something else." Thanks to the little savings I had, I could pay for the room until I left Cuba. Through Ñico I found a job as . . . well, as a servant, if you want to look at it like that. It was at La Campana, a cabaret on Infanta. A very boggy part of town, that's for sure, and swarming with prostitutes. Yankee Marines were a plague there. La Campana was a cabaret where lumpen members of society would go, although good artists did perform there sometimes. The Victoria neighborhood was behind it. It was a neighborhood that had its zenith during World War II to be exact. Almost everything there was a brothel. Some blocks were very quiet, dark, and narrow. They suited the business of prostitution.

At La Campana I didn't stand a snowball's chance in hell. I didn't like the work. I've never been good at waiting on others. But even so, I dealt with a lot of stupid stuff and humiliation. I wasn't a doorman, but a servant. I scrubbed the bathrooms, put out the towels, hung up the jackets on the coat racks. Then they asked me to be a messenger, a go-for between pimps and whores. If I didn't do it, they threw me out. I got medical clearance because no one with a venereal disease could work there that's for sure. And I got my picture taken for the first time in my life at Merallo Studio. It was the first time I've ever seen myself in a photograph. I didn't like the way I looked to tell the truth. I realized that in the photo I couldn't hide the fact that I was a mulatto. My nose stood out and my hair looked like little ringlets because there was so much of it and with the brilliantine. It was *capirro* hair. I sent a copy to my family along with the last letter that I wrote them from Havana.

Since I wasn't working, I'd go around with Miguelito to the neighborhoods by the docks first thing in the morning. We played *caña*, it didn't cost as much as *bolita*. That's what we did with our days. The *caña* game was dangerous. You'd grab a kitchen or butcher's knife, and cut the sugarcane in the center of the stalk in one slash. Whoever cut the lowest would win a piece of cane, or would count up however many *medio real* or *real* coins depending on what the players had on them. That's how poor people would entertain themselves in poor neighborhoods. I really miss the docks despite all the disasters I saw and experienced myself. Because however you'd like it to be, what's yours is yours. There I'd go and ask Eva for a peso. Or I'd say to Ñico, "Why don't you buy me a drink?" and they wouldn't let me down.

But here your neighbor doesn't even look at you. And even though you make a donation, the institutions are the ones that benefit or it magically disappears. Although we've lived here for forty years, that's why we don't forget about Cuba and many of us have refused to become US citizens.

Upon seeing so many boats go in and out of the port, I got the idea to take off in search of another way. Evangelio Amor had gone by boat to Miami running away from El Colorado. He'd send letters to his girlfriends where I lived encouraging them to leave. But Evangelio was a scoundrel. I'm sure he was involved with drugs. Even though he said he sold insurance policies, he was involved with some American mobsters in Havana. I'd see him at La Campana pulling tricks in order to get by. This put a thorn in my side because he had no reason to be there.

Chibás was right in his speeches: corruption reigned. That's why the broom was his symbol. Unemployment was the agenda. Every week many people took a plane to Miami for forty pesos and returned speaking English. Others stayed there illegally and you never saw them again. Speaking of money, Havana became a lupanar as they said in Mexican films. The enchanted paradise of the song "La Habana, princesita del mar" was for fat cats and the rich. If people didn't rob, they were always pawning or had one foot in jail. They had to support their family no matter what.

"Look, Julián. A letter from Evan."

I was reading what he was telling them to say and imagined what it was like. But those women were little doves despite what they'd seen and experienced. They let themselves be sweet-talked by guys who changed their saint and sign every other day. It isn't that I'm more patriotic than Maceo, or anything like that, but I never ever changed my name in this country, never. Some people call me Tony because many Cubans gave themselves the name Tony. They did it to make things easier because their real name was Eustaquio or Salvador, names with no English translation. On the other hand, there was a large number of Cubans with the name Antonio and that's why Tony became the national nickname.

But I wasn't even close to feeling American. One of the things that really caught my attention when I got here was Cuban *guajiros* from Mayarí and Jobabo who gave themselves a name like Frank, Mike, or Tony. Or they'd change their last name like a Park Avenue doorman named Guillermo Guerra, who had the nerve to call himself Billy Battle. Guys without a country, traitors . . . I had nothing to do with them. At least I never understood them or associated with them.

nobember 27 1950

Dear julian

when i got your letta it was the biggest suprise of my life and were all very worried here about what you say your going on a trip in a bot and your gunna send a letta from the country your goin to and you didnt tell us we thought that you have forgot us julian thats why we didnt send you fotos of my and pascuals kids our mother stil thinks you lost your mind and sends you much love like all ways

i work all the time and take care of your nephews and nieces thats all i do julian take care of your self and keep sendin letters im gunna answer you always here every one thinks about you a lot and we know you also think about us but your very bisy in Havana take care there are better hospitals there because here theres nothing to tell about

i love you and think of you   Yara

The idea of Miguelito and me leaving together was taking shape. From talking about it so much, we finally gave in and there was no other way to go. You'd look in one direction and nothing. And then in the other direction, nothing. So north was the only way to go. Many people had already come and things weren't so bad for them according to what they'd say in their letters. But no matter what, the Cuban thing to do is to get here and after a few days have your picture taken on a street in the Bronx or Manhattan in front of a luxury car, wearing a jacket and corduroy hat. That's typical. Or if not that, in front of a five-star hotel and put, "This is where I work." They were lies because whoever got here completely broke and without a trade, had to work hard in a factory and wash lots of dishes.

I met with Eva so she could fill me in. I was already thinking about the trip and she was a woman of the world; she wasn't going to give me bad advice. She said, "Look, Julián, you can stay here rent-free. Clean the patio twice a week and collect from the tenants. I'm not going to die of hunger from seven pesos less a month."

"I appreciate it, Eva, but I want to better my situation, have something of my own, and get to know another country. I'm leaving."

I started to go through the motions. And in the middle of it all two jobs came my way because that's how life works. One as a driver for the Polish guy Michel and the other as a dockworker. But I wasn't interested. I wanted to leave and seek my fortune. My dream was to have my own house, a car, and three or four suits. Miguelito was also already really into it. With one idea in two heads, no one can stop it.

What really got to me was the fire in Cuba's room. The poor thing. They never found out if it was the old man's lit cigarette or if some bandit threw a lighted match through the window. They came to get me from the kiosk on the corner where I'd have a coffee and kill some time. They were screaming that I had to go put out the fire. From the corner you could see the smoke coming out the windows. And as the fire rose, it spread to my room and ruined my mattress and the few clothes I had left. The women looked like frightened hens running up and down Virtudes with nice shoes on, clasping figures of saints in their hands, holding them to their chests.

A fire is always a fire. Especially when the fire truck doesn't even show up. Smoke filled the patio when I went in the main door of the *accesoria*. I shoved a towel in my mouth and managed to put out the flames on Cuba's mattress with a blanket. My eyebrows got scorched. The entire neighborhood went in the tenement with bedspreads, blankets, and towels. I screamed, "Don't throw water on it, don't throw water on it!" but there was someone who threw buckets and more buckets and the fire got bigger and bigger.

Firemen weren't necessary. The fire died down and the scare was greater than the damage. The walls of my room were almost black. There was a strong stench in the air and I went in to save what I could. The only photo I had of Emerlina in the Parque de los Estudiantes was gone. But my shoes survived and I could stuff the mattress with batting from Muralla Street. The stench from the fire lasted for weeks and you couldn't even clean the walls with Fab. The iron bed was the only thing that survived from Cuba's room.

"My sister, the poor little thing, if she saw her room now. Oh, Santa Barbara, help me!"

That's how she was for several days, while the old man got some furniture and comforted her. I helped her to mount the window frames and cover an old mattress. But she was a mess. Everything she had that reminded her of her sister was ash.

"Look, Man, someone is messing with you."

"It's not that, Miguelito. I told you before, fire follows me everywhere I go."

"So try to beat it. You get me?"

And that was what I did starting right then and there. But I haven't always been able to avoid it. No way! I became a hero overnight because I put out a fire all by myself. I'm not exaggerating—people admired me. And I felt that for the first time in my life I'd done something important. I was proud, because I wasn't a fireman and I had put out a fire. I couldn't shut up about it for a month. And when I'd tell people the story, they'd open their eyes really wide and pat me on the back. You always exaggerate a little, that's true.

Life in Havana was getting out of one problem and into another. There was no way to get ahead. And I wasn't Daniel Santos, nor did I have the makings of a pimp or a tough guy. I learned to read and write, but I didn't make it to second grade because I started to work as soon as possible. That's why I understood prostitutes. They were victims of society. And many of them would spend almost their entire salary on money orders for their families.

"Julián, I send money to my younger sisters and brothers. That's all I think about. That's why I can't get sick or involved with only one man. I have to keep doing this even though I don't like it. You know what the countryside is like. If it weren't for my job, my family would starve to death."

Then, they'd take a swig of rum and start to cry or sing *Muñequita linda* on the patio with all their might. Almost all of them would do the same thing. There's no doubt about it, they were bandits and ungrateful, but most of them were unfortunate. They were exploited by tough guys and pimps and heard a bunch of nonsense talk from repugnant, old men and perverts. I treated them like human beings in Havana. And when I got here and saw them swarming the corners, dressed the same way, with the same colors, the same flowers in their hair, the same walk, and even younger, I realized, as the saying goes, that it is the oldest profession in the world.

I've never been a hypocrite or tried to put a band-aid on a gaping wound. The truth is difficult and you got to face it. I've never lived with my head in clouds. Maybe that's why I've been courageous enough to confront my destiny. I've never discriminated, nor have I ever just watched someone suffer. I've also never said "never." I've had my dreams about life this country, that's for sure, and they were crushed. But, what else could I've done? Even though I got here ready for anything and with the desire to get ahead, I went through a lot like everyone else. And that's what I can talk about here. Not about the lies, or the fiction that many people invent, rather about a true story.

Emigration

You can't make a home in a foreign land.

In Cuba news travels like lightening. Nothing's a secret for long because Cubans are blabbermouths. They usually don't have bad intentions; they're just very curious and like to get involved in other people's business when they shouldn't. I've met women who've let gossip destroy their marriages and men who've lost their jobs because they couldn't keep their mouths shut. Miguelito and I didn't spread the word about the trip because people would think we had money and come hustle us just to get a dime. In Havana, there are just as many professional hustlers and blackmailers as stray dogs. They'd come up to you with some bullshit story and say, "My child's dying from diphtheria."

It wasn't true; they had no kids. If you gave them a peso they'd get lost and go sleep under the Almendares Bridge and you wouldn't see them in the neighborhood ever again. Although I've never been all that political, I've always believed that if you don't work, you don't eat. Life in Havana was hard, but unemployment is one thing and laziness another. These people had a certain look about them and were almost always involved in some political brawl.

Eva told the entire *solar* that Miguelito and I planned to go work in the United States. So one night Cuba's husband came up to my room and gave me a leather suitcase: "This'll save you some money, Julián. It doesn't look like Cuba's going to see her sister. Take the suitcase and good luck."

Then he asked me if I was really going with José Mujica. It really made me laugh because the difference between Miguelito Cuesta and Mujica was night and day.

"I don't get money from the government and I don't sell drugs," I told him. "And Miguelito's thinking about going to sing on Broadway. We'll see what happens."

"To each his own," he responded. "To each his own."

Americans invested a billion dollars in Cuba. We were the White House's patio with palm trees. The government was getting rid of leftist unions on a daily basis. There wasn't much to look forward to. Miguelito's brother brought us up to date on the situation. We'd have to go all the way to Juanelo just to see him because he had a clandestine lifestyle back then. They accused him of setting a store on fire in Mariano and he denied it. They made him out to be a communist. That was all. He didn't explicitly tell us to "leave," but he certainly didn't stop us. Miguelito was in the shithouse because he didn't know how to save money.

"We blacks don't save, Julián. That's something you guys, the mulattos, do to be like white people."

I didn't put my money in a bank, but I did have a piggy bank for the trip because I was set on going. A few days before leaving when we had almost everything ready to go and Ñico had given each of us a coat, Miguelito shows up at my place with some story about a man on Concepción de la Valla Street who heard him sing and was going to give him voice lessons for free. He was set on becoming an artist and wouldn't let anyone twist his arm. But it was a scam. His lessons were going well and the teacher was good, but he wasn't the only student. It was a voice school and not an employment agency. The entire thing totally destroyed Miguelito's life in Havana. He stopped selling sugarcane. He stopped looking for a job. He didn't even care about his woman anymore . . . He didn't even realize what the heck was going on until I opened his eyes.

I go talk to his teacher:

"Tell me, Teacher, does he have what it takes?"

"Well, Son, he does have what it takes, but I see many just like him every day."

"So, he's wasting his time, right?"

"Well, I wouldn't call it that. He does sing with the others . . . I have students who've been here for over twenty years taking classes and they never give up. They want to be artists. It's as simple as that."

I've never seen anyone with that kind of determination, but at the same time I've never met someone with shittier luck.

"Talk him out of it," his woman told me. But I couldn't. He was confident that he was going to be successful in a profession saturated with guys just like him. I was going to the place on Concepción de la Valla for a few weeks. I fell in love with a cute little mulatta named Lidia Margarita Amorós. She was a singer, and just like Miguelito, unemployed and set on making it as an artist. She could pay for the classes though because her mother was a seamstress and her father was a driver. One day I wanted to bring her back to my room, the most natural thing in the world, and the cute little mulatta told her old man, a beast, and he told the teacher not to let me in the place anymore.

One day the teacher said to me: "You're hurting me. This isn't good for business." Out of respect, I stopped going to Concepción de la Valla. It was a loony bin. At the time it was everyone's dream to be on television. However, they didn't know that television and radio were both controlled by the sponsors, and if you weren't liked, no one even looked at you. That's why so many singers left Cuba for Latin America and Europe. Skin color was also important. In order to get anywhere, you needed the support of a political party, a station, or a councilman from a very influential neighborhood. Miguelito was the captain of the boat until it sank. When he was convinced that north was the only way to go, he said to me:

"Let's go, I feel really bad leaving my woman, but . . ."

"You'll send for her when you have the money. I'll help you."

"You wouldn't want to leave her on her own, Julián. I get it."

This is the kind of thing you don't want to do alone, that's for sure. In spite of everything, Miguelito was generally happier and more daring than I was. And I knew his attitude would help me through the rough times. As the people from the countryside say "if you have a friend, you have a horse, and if you have a horse, you have a hundred pesos." I waited until he made up his mind for sure, although mentally I was already there.

I went to say goodbye to Matilde at the hat shop. In one afternoon I made all the rounds. I went to see Méndez, the barber, and Ñico: the ones who helped me out in Havana. Everyone was happy for me and wished me the best of luck. It was Petronila who told me as if it were a secret:

"Don't get your hopes up."

You appreciate it when someone tells you something like that because you realize there are sincere people in the world.

"Don't forget about your country. Everything is very pretty at first over there, but here is where you'll always find human warmth," she stressed to me. That was good advice. That's why I still feel so Cuban today despite the distance. And although I have residency and already paid my dues here, when they say to me: "Cuban-American?"

I say: "No. Only Cuban."

I've gotten into fights with some bastards over it. There are those who are proud to be American citizens, although they were born in Latin America and have their roots there. I see them speaking broken English, wanting to pass for gringos. They're traitors. They're just wasting their time because here a Hispanic is a Hispanic no matter what. Before they were called spicks, the most contemptuous, the lowest category. Now it's Hispanic and more or less it's the same dog with a different collar. That's why I'm proud to be a Cuban and to have my roots there. However, I'm going to die here because I'm too old to start a new life. And

I'm not going to be a public burden where I haven't even lifted a finger. My arthritis is so bad that I can hardly move from the waist down, that's why I do mostly everything with my hands. But lately my fingers have gotten pretty swollen, and even though they don't hurt, I can barely move them. They're good for nothing. The same thing happens with my memory. Perhaps it's premature aging. Or it could be that I don't find much purpose in life anymore and from doing nothing my brain falls asleep. I don't know. I don't want to think about it too much because I always try to see the good side of things. I'm like this for a reason.

I sold everything. Just like the Arabs do, I put all my belongings out on my doorstep except for my wristwatch and white shoes. I gave everything away for practically nothing. Women bought things for their husbands. I gave Cuba winter pants that were a gift from the Polish guy Michel, and I left her the table and chairs along with the mattress and bed. I sold the refrigerator to Eva for half price. She said, "I'm going to miss you, Julián." She had big black bulging eyes and a cigarette hanging out of her mouth all the time.

"I'll miss you too, Eva. You've been very good to me." She laughed. She always laughed as if there were something fishy in what I was saying, or as if she were partly making fun of me. I really didn't get it. Arabs are like that. However, life taught me to respect them because they are determined. Here in New York they've worked a lot and it hasn't been easy for them. I always think about good old Eva when I'm in a bad mood or going through a rough time. I don't know how she managed, but she always held herself together. It must've been her desire to live, her attachment to things. We Cubans are a little like that. We could bell the cat and then forget about it. And people would think we're winners. We give the impression that we're on top of it all. It's better that way. Don't you think? It'd be bad if you were seen crying under a banana plant. No one needs to see that stuff. I've always tried to dress well and hold my head very high, even when I'd go hungry.

Poverty begs for attention, as my grandmother Juana la Callá would say. I learned from Eva to always hold my head very high.

I always say to my wife: "If you only had the will of Eva la Libanesa, . . ." Celia is very good like most Boricuas, but she's missing that strong desire to keep going. It always seems to me that she's going to die tomorrow, I don't know. It's her blood. It's thin like horchata. But that's a story for another day. Now I'm going to tell about how I finally got Miguelito Cuesta to leave Havana and what I had to do to get him to budge . . .

Miguelito can be a little sly. Without saying a word to me, he was sending resumes to New York. He sent some to film studios, electrician schools, and language schools in Jackson Heights. So if they didn't take him as an extra, he could take a course for electricians but he'd have to know a little English. Everyone spoke broken English in Havana. Everyone knew the basics to take tourists around Colón or sell them trinkets in the Prado. Miguelito and I had talked a good deal about it: knowing the language was a very serious thing and in order to study it, you had to enroll in a school. That crafty devil sent resumes and all the answers were: "Good" or "Very good." Then they asked him for a picture of himself. What was he going to do? Just close his eyes and send them something? When they saw that he was as black as night, they stopped answering him. That's when it all ended. That's why the trip was always on his mind. When he finally confessed, I said to him:

"You don't think that it'll be different for me?"

"No, Julián, you're a light-skinned mulatto. You pass."

But it wasn't like that: here, no one passes. If you have one single drop of black blood in your veins, and it shows, you're black in this country. Even the white and blond Puerto Ricans were labeled "Black" on their ration cards. Felipe Colón, a friend of mine, was a clerk at a clothing store. One day we went together to sign up for a course for refrigeration technicians and they asked us to state our nationality. I said "Cuban" and they put down: "Cuban, Black." He said Puerto Rican and they put the same thing for him: "Puerto

Rican, Black." His hair was light brown and his skin as white as snow. He said: "No, I'm Puerto Rican. Nothing else." The secretary reluctantly erased the word "Black."

It was time to leave. There was no turning back. And finally, after all that non-sense, we got our papers and arrived in Tampa on December 28, 1951.

Miguelito wanted to go by boat. In those years the *Florida*, an old ferry that made weekend trips, and the *Cuba* left from the port of Havana. But I wanted to fly because it was faster and more practical. I eventually got him excited about it. I dragged him out of his place at 205 Paula Street by his ear. His woman wouldn't let him leave. She was totally against it. She said she was going to curse him. She told him: "You're cursed by someone who committed suicide. If you don't free yourself of it, things are going to go really bad for you." It was a joke. Finally, with the money and our papers all ready, we went to the American Embassy in the Plaza de Armas and applied for a twenty-nine-day visa. Miguelito's woman figured out everything that was going on. He really didn't want to leave her but at the same time he didn't tell her he'd definitely send for her. The visa took a few days. A tourist visa, of course. Once we had it in our hands we went to the Pan American Airways ticket agency and got a direct flight to Tampa. Miguelito had some friends there who were tobacco rollers. Michel's sister, Luba, had also lived there since 1943. I gave her a letter of recommendation from her brother and a white sweater that Ana knitted herself.

When I got on the airplane, I couldn't believe it. It was a hop, skip, and a jump away. Orange juice, sandwiches, candies, and we were in Florida. The Tampa airport was like a cardboard box. It was scary. We got a taxi and went to a Cuban boarding house in Ibor City, where Martí had been. The neighborhood was still full of Cubans.

"Get that look off your face," I told Miguelito.

"Leave me alone, Julián. Just leave me alone."

I don't know what happened to him, but he looked different. The trip was no big deal. The temperature was good; cool, gentle breeze. The stop over in Florida was more or less temporary. We were there for twenty-nine days legally and about three or four months illegally. They gave us a B-29 for having stayed past the twenty-nine days without arranging the proper paperwork. B-29 was the password for the undocumented. The name came from some old World War II airplanes. They were bombers used to transport the immigrants who didn't abide by the law to Ellis Island. Luckily, we never landed there. Ellis Island was the Detention Center for those without papers. A couple of immigration agents would ask for I.D., and if they didn't show it, straight to Ellis Island. They were there for a few days and then sent back to wherever they came from. Generally they paid for the trip, because if they returned at the expense of their country, they were in dire straits and would then get the documents together once again. I met a bunch of people from Ellis Island.

But, I'll say it again, Miguelito and I weren't taken away because we were clean in Tampa. We were illegal just that one time, but we both got passable letters of recommendation and returned to Havana on another Pan American flight to get our permanent visas at the US Embassy. In other words, we had to do everything legally.

I had a letter from a Catalan man who owned a pastry shop, and another one from Luba. Miguelito got something similar from his tobacco-roller friends. We were in Havana for a few days. With the money I had, I stayed in the Bristol Hotel and bought presents for my friends. Miguelito was living it up with his wife, going from bar to bar. He lost the sheet with the digital fingerprints from the district police. It was a huge mess, but with some money he was able to get false fingerprints. The embassy didn't even notice.

That's how we made it back to Tampa and with one hundred bucks in our pockets to get into the country. I went to Luba's house and he went to his tobacco-roller friends' place. But Tampa was only a bridge to New York. I worked in the Spanish pastry shop there and lived with the Polish woman until one day when she wanted me to marry her. I gave her a big fat "NO." I was only thirty at the time and the world was all mine. I wasn't going to stay in an apartment in Tampa with a woman who was twice my age.

I ran out on her. When I had things figured out in New York, I got Miguelito a job in a factory and sent for him. Tampa was a lot like Marianao. The climate was very good, but life there was very boring. It was for old, retired people or well-to-do families. They went there to enjoy the weather when they couldn't think of anything better to do than sit in the sun and drink piña coladas.

I was completely wrecked when I got to New York. I'd downed a bottle of rum before leaving and then drank eight beers on the Greyhound. When the bus finally pulled into the station, I was drunk as a skunk. Manhattan glowed like a giant firefly. Back then the bus stop was on 50th and 7th Avenue. It was a human anthill. It was bone-chilling cold and my coat was paper-thin. My face looked like a tomato. I couldn't feel my ears or my fingers tips. Everything was covered in mist. The snow turned into black ice so it was very dangerous to walk.

With my suitcase in hand and a couple of dollars in my pocket, I started walking towards 20th Street. I had a connection there. This man was supposedly going to rent me a furnished room. The cold sobered me up real fast. I only realized I was in New York when I saw the tip of the Empire State Building on my way downtown. I wasn't positive if it was the Empire State Building or not. I asked a Latino kid because I didn't speak English. He answered in English:

"Yeah, that's it."

In this city you can ask the most idiotic questions in the world, dress like a complete fool, and no one gives a damn. Not even one single person noticed me with my suitcase shivering in the cold. I made it to 6th Avenue and headed towards 20th. I bought some wool gloves at a little stand run by a Chinese man and went in and out of delis and leather-good shops to warm up a bit. As you walk down 6th you leave behind the tallest buildings. Once in a while I put down my suitcase and turned around to look at them. It seemed unreal that I was going to live in a city with those buildings. Some were scary. Some looked like dragons. Others, like the Flat Iron, looked like a chocolate wedge. This was before they put up 6th Avenue's tallest buildings: those ones made of sheet metal and black glass.

There was a crowd on a corner of 23rd. I got closer and saw a warm cadaver covered with a blanket. It was a very pale old man with freckles and red hair. He jumped from the sixteenth floor. I've never seen anything like it. His toupee, full of blood, had fallen off and there it was, next to his keys and scarf. A Latino must have heard me when I said out loud in Spanish:

"What happened?"

"Someone who got tired of the same old song and dance," he answered in Spanish and went on his way. No one touched the dead man until the police got there with the ambulance. He was taken away on a stretcher. I continued walking. It was impressive to see how there was always someone who spoke Spanish in a group of people.

At first, I thought New York was really something else. Since the city is so big and it's impossible to be all over the place, people stay in one area. That's how the ghettos you always hear about are formed. I haven't been to other cities, but I'm sure it's difficult to find one where there's such a racial mix like this one. That's why they call it the Tower of Babel. In Tampa an olive-skinned woman is Hispanic, but here that's not the case: an olive-skinned woman can be Greek or Italian or whatever. It's still that way.

I sometimes get confused with the languages. I'll go to Church or 14th Street to buy something. I start speaking Spanish thinking that I'm talking to a Hispanic, and it turns out that he or she's from Syria or Portugal. That's why Latinos live in El Barrio. They want to be with friends and feel comfortable. It's also because Latinos can't find housing under $500 anywhere else in Manhattan. Hispanics usually have a lot of children. No one wants to rent an apartment to a family with four or five kids. It's a headache to live in Manhattan with an empty wallet.

When I got to New York, another thing caught my attention: the numbers runner, *el bolitero*. In every Hispanic neighborhood, just like in Cuba, there was a man pointing at the little ball with his shiny white shoes, gold chains, and hat; a real *chuchero* in New York. No matter what, Cubans stand out wherever they are because of the way they talk and dress. Cubans are open, talkative, and like to show off. Although Puerto Ricans, or Boricuas as they say, look like Cubans, they are more set in their ways and don't talk as much. They think about things a little too much, I suppose. Cubans don't think about things too much. Boricuas overheat about every stupid thing. Although we have a lot in common, there's a difference. As the saying goes, don't plant yucca in the yam field.

You have to remember that they're oppressed. Almost all of Puerto Rico's working class migrated to the United States in search of work. That has drained the people: they're divided. It's a complicated situation. Although every day the number of people in favor of independence does increase, I hope.

I went to see Ñico's brother-in-law, a guy named José Díaz. He's an old jeweler. A very good person. He invited me to his house on 20th and 8th. He was a cranky old widower, but helpful. He gave me a Cuban coffee and a smoke, and a Chinese horoscope calendar for the year of the rat as a present.

"You come here to work and that's it," he said. Then he asked me questions and told me his life story. I still have yet to meet a Cuban who misses the opportunity to tell his life story!

"So, how are things going for my brother-in-law?"

"Alright. He doesn't do much, José. He says he's not going anywhere."

"He's got a point. The only thing that I've done here is work. Now I'm a widower. I have Social Security and this room, but I would've preferred to live over there. You'll see, Julián, you can't make a home in a foreign land."

José's room was very small, but nice and warm. I sipped my coffee while he showed me his workshop. He'd spent his life grinding silver, working for Jews.

"You can squeeze more oil out of a brick than a Jew," he said to me with a mean face. Then he looked me up and down as if he wanted to say: "This isn't a job for you." I knew it because I've always been pretty clever even though I don't have much schooling. I have a tough look and rough, thick hands; they weren't the hands of a jeweler's apprentice. I was looking all around and, like the grumpy old man that he was, he said to me:

"You're not cut out for this. Don't touch."

He half-heartedly read the letter from Ñico, prepared a big pot of coffee and began his story:

I arrived in '28. Machado was just reelected by force. There was no work in Cuba. Everything was the sounds of son from El Oriente, the Trio Matamoros, carousing and gambling. All of that, but no work. I never got involved with that stuff. That's why I came here. Here drugs were already the order of the day, but there was more work. In Jovellanos, where I'm from, you couldn't make a living. One night when I was a child, my father put the family on a train. I remember it like a dream. It was the year of the bubonic plague in Cuba. We left the farm in La Luisa with our suitcases and went to the town of Palos. My father earned some money wallpapering houses. Back then people covered up the gaps around windows with paper and used sulfur as a disinfectant. They weren't really houses, they were more like poor people's shacks, but it was necessary to try to stop the spread somehow. I came to Key West on the steamship *Cuba*. From there I rented a monster Chandler with five other Latino guys. It cost $25 each.

Here in New York I lived in a room on 23rd Street with an Ecuadorian from Río Bamba and two Chileans. I was the only one who had my own cot. I bought it for a couple of dollars. The owner of the house was a promiscuous French woman. Although she wasn't officially a whore, she had been married five times. Then she fell in love with the Ecuadorian and dressed him up in a topcoat and umbrella. I started off washing dishes on 50th and Broadway for $17 a week. Then I made a change. I got a job in a button factory putting enamel on buttons. The job required great skill although it paid next to nothing. You have to learn everything in order to live in New York; I figured that out right away and became a carpenter. I framed windows and made my own furniture. I learned everything there is to know about shoemaking, electric wiring, and plumbing. I wasn't going to give money away to any bastard. That's what you got to do here, Julián, if not, you'll pay through the nose for being a newcomer.

I was too ambitious and failed in the jewelry business. When I had my workshop up and running, a Chilean came to sell me a thousand books at five cents a piece. I bought them thinking I could resell them, but because I didn't know English and never even read a book from cover to cover, I threw the money away because the books were trash. They didn't sell and I had to go to a dump and burn them at the end of the year. If you're too greedy, you break the bank. Here you have to specialize in something; there's no other way.

We had another coffee and some cake. Díaz told me all about the Julio Antonio Mella Club. He was a good conversationalist.

I learned to make jewelry and speak English all on my own. I picked up the little I know by listening to people on the street. In the button factory, they spoke Spanish and Italian, so I guess you could say I learned English on the subway. When jewelry making wasn't going so well, I'd go work at the factory. I met several Cubans there. Some were communists escaping Machado. The factory was at 108 Wooster Street. It belonged to Catalans. We perforated plastic sheets and buttons, a job for ladies. I made $30 a week, a good salary, and with overtime we'd get $60. The Julio Antonio Mella Club was already there and, one of the Cubans, Enrique Pérez Oliva, would say to me every day: "Come on, Pepe. Let's go." But others said that because it was a communist club, the members would get rowdy all the time and the police were always giving them trouble. I didn't want to get involved with that mess so I didn't go to the Mella Club until well into the 30s. Mentioning the word "communist" before that was really something. Enrique never said anything to me about it until he returned to Cuba. He didn't make it here. I had to get him on the button-decorating shift. He was a very good activist, but knew nothing about craftsmanship. He worked to eat.

The Mella Club was an important group here. I served on the Board of Directors, and on the Recreation and Decoration committees. That's where I'd go most of the time. There were also other places that hosted dances and dinners: the Mexican Women Workers Mutual, the Spanish Workers Club, the Cuban Club . . . There were a bunch of them, but I preferred the Mella Club because there you learned about politics. It was a three-story building with a bar downstairs. They had the best and the cheapest Latino food there: fried plantains, chicken and rice, black beans, tamales, you name it . . . On the third floor, they had a dance floor and a conference room. That's where I learned what being a worker was all about. I realized that no political party was doing anything for workers. The Liberals had lost all respect. The Conservatives were for the ones who already had it all. The Republicans were pure demagogues. The Democrats were weak, a party for housewives. I read a pamphlet by Julio Antonio Mella that said it all. I had that thing for about twenty years, but then I lost it. Julio Antonio explained very clearly the struggle between bosses and workers. He said: "Bosses cause disagreements among workers, causing them to fight."That's when we began to open our eyes.

Pablo de la Torriente Brau spoke many times at the club. And so did the North American revolutionary leader James Ford. But Pablo was the best speaker, he was so passionate. He'd climb up onto a chair and deliver a speech that would win everyone over. I'll never forget the time he yelled at the top of his lungs: "Workers of the world, unite."The audience stood up right away and sang *La Internacional*. He died in the Spanish Civil War. I cut out a photo of him wearing a black beret from *Bohemia* magazine.

José was a strong and very lively man. His bad temper would come out when someone stuck their nose in his business. He didn't want to teach me jewelry making, but he did get me cheap housing and a job. But he'd always say to me:

"The honest jeweler starves to death, My Friend. You need money to make jewelry, and to get money you've got to steal."

He introduced me to a Cuban from Vueltas named Plácido. He was a leftist and worked as a super in a building on 19th, a street in Chelsea full of warehouses. I set up shop in this city between a firehouse and a furrier's warehouse. It was a Latino neighborhood, like Little Spain. I mean the old Little Spain, the one that used to be where Lincoln Center is today. I paid $10 a week for a room without a bathroom, but it was completely private. Díaz had found work for me in a Latino restaurant in Chelsea. It was called El Liborio. I earned $20 a week as a busboy. I couldn't be a waiter because I didn't even know one single sentence in English.

The language thing drove me crazy. There where nights when I'd go home alone to my place. I didn't want to talk to anybody, I was so mad that I couldn't even say "What do you want, Sir?" It wouldn't come out. I heard it over and over again, but just couldn't get it. I was good for nothing when it came to languages. I still can hardly speak it. I know phrases, certain sayings, and even complete proverbs, but they don't get me through an entire evening because I get tongue-tied. That was always my biggest challenge in this country. But there's no use crying over spilt milk. Almost everyone speaks Spanish here. I'm proud to be Cuban and I speak my language so that everyone can hear me. Before it was a tragedy for me not being able to say a thing. I know not speaking English held me back several times.

The day someone tried to set my room on fire, I screamed: "Fire! Fire!" When the police came, I called José, who lived around the block, so he could help me. A wise-ass Colombian from the third floor wanted to get me out of there because his Cuban wife had run around behind his back with an American jockey. To get revenge, and because I didn't say "Good morning" or anything to him, he got an old armchair and laced it with alcohol. He put it in front of the door to my room while I was sleeping. He threw a match on it. The old armchair immediately went up in flames and burned part of my door. Luckily, I smelled the smoke and could put the fire out with blankets I had in the house. And I stuck my head out the window. Since the firehouse was the next building over, the firemen put out the rest of the flames right away with a white, foamy liquid, but the door was damaged and I had to rebuild it. When I told Díaz about the incident, he said, "This is just the beginning, Julián. You've got to pay a high price to make ends meet in this country."

The Colombian disappeared for a few days and I couldn't track him down because I was working all the time. A month later, I ran into him in the stairway as if nothing had happened. I didn't say anything to him because I didn't have proof that he'd done anything, but I gave him the look of death. That really made him quiver. He was one of the first to go down when the cocaine dealers were raided by the Mayor of New York in 1951. I never saw him again.

The room was small, but warm. The kerosene heat stunk and made a coating on the walls and gave off terrible smoke. The place needed furniture, a refrigerator and a good mattress. I ripped down the shelves in the room because the previous renter, a filthy old Catalan, had made them with codfish boxes to save on wood, and the smell was unbearable. Díaz gave me a can of green paint and I gave the room two coats. I got rid of one smell and created another. I almost poisoned myself that January. No one opened their windows. Between the cold and the smell of paint, I thought I was dying. "The bastard was smart to stay in Tampa," I said to myself when I thought about Miguelito. But that wasn't the case. A few days later a letter from him arrived at Díaz's place. In it he asked me to find him work here because Tampa was a mosquito farm. Miguelito still wanted to make it as an artist. He wanted to sing on Broadway. And he didn't know that here simply wanting to do something wasn't enough. I told him, "Be patient, My Friend," and I went to talk to Díaz.

"I already know what you want. You're looking for a job for your friend in Tampa. Ñico recommended him, but that doesn't mean much. He's twice as dark as you are, right?"

"But what about scrubbing floors? Washing dishes?"

"Sometimes they don't even want them for that. Let's see. For now, get yourself settled here."

Plácido turned on the hot water once a week, usually on a Saturday. The other days we heated it up in pots or buckets that we all used. The bathroom was close, but everyone froze. You'd be shivering to death once you got there. The apartments with a kitchen, like the one I got later, had a bathtub in the living room. That was a plus. You didn't have to go out in the hallway where the rats milled around. Some were as big as cats. Living conditions were horrendous in poor neighborhoods. The houses were old and the linoleum floors swelled when it was humid, then they'd crack, and the holes would turn into roach nests. You couldn't sleep because of the noise from the hot water pipes. When the water would run through the pipes, it'd come crashing down. It sounded like Niagara Falls was in your room. In Havana you got an idea about this country, but when you saw how it really was, your heart dropped.

I lucked out with Plácido. Even though I was clean, no criminal history, no drug history, the district police always searched my room when a neighbor would move to El Barrio.

The famous New York mayor Fiorello La Guardia cracked down on opium smokers. When a super wanted to get rid of someone, he got the precinct police to mess with them. They'd have to leave, no questions asked. It was a blessing to know José Díaz in New York. He highly recommended me and so no one messed with me. Plácido was my fellow countryman and a law-abiding citizen. But I met many shameless supers. Some would put marijuana in a resident's dresser drawer and then call the police. That's what they'd do when they wanted to kick someone out. Many dirty tricks have been played on Puerto Ricans in this country. LaGuardia cleaned things up a bit. Today, evil runs rampant. It's everywhere. No one gets scared. No one goes in their houses. People are on the street risking their lives because mafiosos and murderers rule in this city.

Years back the name LaGuardia meant something. Now it's just another airport in New York. I remember stories about LaGuardia going into a neighborhood and being able to get things in order with his spirit. Or he'd get on the fire truck with a helmet on his head to go put out a fire. He'd even dress up as a traffic cop. He was like a democratic king: he found out about the poor and went to see for himself what was going on in the most dangerous neighborhoods. He got on the subway. He went up to Harlem. The current mayor only makes TV appearances and doesn't even say "Merry Christmas."

New York is a dangerous place. It's a shame because the city has a lot to offer, but it's no longer safe. One of my friends was robbed of everything not even a week ago. He was an older man, he didn't have much. Now he wants to appeal to Welfare in order to get his things back, we'll see . . . They even took the refrigerator. The cat was the only thing they left him with. This happens a lot here. That's why stores that sell alarms and locks have made a killing in the last years.

With my first month's pay I went down to Houston Street to look for a second-hand refrigerator. The Bowery was at its height. Drunks gathered on the corners downing pure alcohol out of small glass bottles, panhandling and cleaning windshields with filthy, old rags. They'd press the button so that the light would turn red and then swarmed the cars like flies. It's the same way today, but it really caught my attention when I first got here. They didn't work; they didn't eat; they slept on the street, in the cold, covered with newspapers and rice sacks. When I saw all those people on the Lower East Side, I felt a little better about my situation. I said to myself: "Shit, they're much worse off than I am."

José went with me to buy the refrigerator. It was cheap because I bought it used and broken. We rewired the machine, gave it new rubber lining and painted it. It really made my life a lot easier. I could hardly believe that it was all mine. Before I got it, I had to keep the milk and meat cool on the windowsill. Then I went to the East Side to get a second-hand mattress. I folded it and carried it uphill. I walked from 60-something and Lexington to my house on 19th and 8th. I was spent when I got home. I threw myself on that mattress and slept like a baby until the next day.

My first snowfall. I kind of liked it. The snow is very pretty the first day, when it falls and lies on the awnings and cars like shaved coconut. Then it becomes dirty and turns into hard chunks of ice on the curbs and stoops and in the puddles. I fell several times because this was all new to me. It can be very dangerous because you don't stop slipping and sliding. You lose all control and can easily crack a rib or split your head open. When I got to the restaurant my boss made me shovel the snow in front. Since there was no work contract or anything like it, I had to do it without making a fuss. My fingers froze and I thought the tips were going to fall off. The cold went right through my gloves. My bones rattled and my face turned beet red. I bought a pair of woolen long johns in a thrift store. I only took them off to wash them. They didn't even do anything: the cold was inside of me. Salt melts the snow, but the slush has to be scraped with shovels or rakes.

A busboy is nothing more than a servant. Sometimes I even had to wash the dishes in the kitchen or clean the entire restaurant. I couldn't say a thing about it because Puerto Ricans were lined up right behind me just waiting for a job in a restaurant. I bought myself a hand sink with my tips. Plácido let me install it in my room because we became friends. He knew how clean we Cubans are. I gave myself a sponge bath every day from head to toe. He'd say: "I'm going to keep a tab on you for the next few months." But it was a habit. That's why I bought a bathtub when I gained some weight. I put it next to the bed. Then I no longer had to leave my place to take a bath. It was a big relief, a real comfort.

Many people used to go to the public baths on 57th and 9th or in the Village. I never went because I had my own bathtub and sink. But I did go to the pool with many Puerto Rican friends, or Boricuas. It was at a hotel in Brooklyn and not expensive at all. I met many Latinos there and picked up some very good-looking women. It was a big indoor pool with deliciously warm water. One day it was filled with blood. Blacks from El Barrio started to come. Of course, it was their right to be there, but the Italians didn't like it at all. There were violent protests, but I kept a low profile in order to avoid an argument.

"You're not the problem, Julián," a Dominican friend told me.

I wasn't from El Barrio and I wasn't charcoal black, but I was still colored. They never said anything to me and they didn't give me dirty looks, but they did to the others. They just stepped foot in the place and war broke out. They never went out alone. They traveled in groups, like a tribe, in order to feel protected and ready to fight if need be.

One night, around nine—it was just about closing time—an Italian and a black guy from Harlem started cursing at each other. A beer bottle flew through the air. The Italian drew a switchblade and threatened the black guy from the edge of the pool. Another black guy grabbed the Italian by the neck and stabbed him in the back as he was falling into the water. There was no security on duty. The pool turned into a bloodbath.

Everyone screamed, some just for the sake of it. Women ran from one side of the pool to the other, but no one went in to help them get out. They barely made it up the stepladder and collapsed and bled at the edge of the pool. Everyone blamed the black man. Racism has always been an issue here. When I was summoned as a witness, I just told what I saw. It was the Italian's fault, but no one wanted to admit it. He provoked the situation by showing off, just like a Cuban. The blacks took the case to court and won. Very few, however, kept going to the Brooklyn pool.

My situation was different. Even though my skin is dark, it's not black. I don't mean to say that I can pass for white, but I'm a light mulatto with wavy hair. Now that my hair is gray, it's softer. It really doesn't make a difference to me.

Plácido and I didn't see each other all that often. Work at El Liborio was tiring. I'd be running around all day, without a chance to catch my breath and no breaks until my shift ended. It wasn't so bad on a good night. Sometimes the customers would even leave me tickets for a Broadway show. I wasn't a theater fan, although I did see a show every once in a while. Sometimes the Broadway artists would come to El Liborio. I think they were mostly from the chorus. They were wild about Cuban food and drank rum out of beer glasses. Since I made a fuss over them they'd ask me, "When's your birthday, Julián?" and then they'd give me tickets. Naturally, I invented monthly birthdays for myself. Then I'd scalp the orchestra seats or standing room tickets outside Schubert Alley or Plymouth Theater. I almost never went because I knew I'd fall asleep in those comfy seats. In those years, Tallulah Bankhead, Mary Martin, and Ann Miller were the hits on Broadway. They were all over the newspapers and commercials.

One night Plácido showed up at my place with a copy of *The Daily Worker*, the communist newspaper in the US. He read me the headlines and said, "It's one of the few newspapers you can trust.

The mafia controls almost all the others." The *The Daily Worker* is now called *The Daily World*. It was founded in 1924. Once in a while, Plácido would come over and read me the headlines. But since I didn't know English, I bought *La Prensa* or *El Imparcial* when I wanted to find out the details of some crime. Saturday afternoons, before going to the restaurant, I'd go to Central Park to watch the people play baseball. A bunch of Hispanics would get together in the park. Baseball is Cuba's national sport, and although I wasn't such a fan, at least it was somewhat entertaining and didn't cost a dime. I'd bundled up from head to toe. The cold was unbearable. However, it wasn't that bad because it's true that you can get used to anything.

Plácido showed me around New York. He told me about the movies on 42nd Street, the theaters that now cost $5. Before you could see not one, but two films for thirty-five cents before six in the evening. Then at six the ticket price went up to seventy-five cents, and not only was it more expensive, but also more danger-ous. At that hour all types of brawls went on in those 42nd Street movie houses. Once I saw a white guy crack a black man's jaw just because he sat next to his wife. It was better to go to the movies in the afternoon: you paid less and avoided problems like that. But speaking of money, I didn't get to enjoy myself very much during those first weeks. I didn't have the time or the energy to go out in the snow when it was minus thirteen- or fifteen-degree weather.

I talked to Plácido about Miguelito and he gave me a pretty good idea. Since the owner of the restaurant already knew me and knew that I was reliable, Plácido suggested I tell him about Miguelito. Cubans in those years were sought out, not because we were liked, but because we were hard workers. I went right up to my boss and told him what was on my mind: "Those who wait, get the dregs."

"Don't bring him in just yet," he told me.

I wrote Miguelito to tell him the good news, and he answered right away, thanking me. After a month, the owner told me to bring him in to replace me because I was going to become a waiter.

I already knew the names of the dishes in English. I could even say "bread and butter." But at El Liborio you didn't need to speak English because most of the customers, even the Americans, spoke Spanish. They liked to show off in front of their guests and practice their Spanish. It was a popular, neighborhood restaurant, nothing fancy. Plácido let Miguelito stay in my room for a week. I thanked him very much because I didn't know if he'd have money or not, since he was a stray bullet. But he did have some money and we were able to find him a shared room a few blocks from my place with a Venezuelan guy who'd just gotten here. It was more or less a room like mine, but with no heat.

"Hey, Julián, is it always this cold?"

"Yup, but you'll get used to it, Miguelito, you'll see."

Blacks turned white in the cold; their skin becomes cracked and chaffed. The blacker you are, the more you feel the cold.

"I won't make it here, Julián."

"Yes, you will, Brother. Get another blanket and a hat to cover your ears."

He got used to it like everyone else. He learned how to be a busboy in a flash. He made more tips in one week than what I earned in three months. He was a whiz at the job, but he still really wanted to sing and tap dance. But just because he lived in New York, didn't mean he was an artist: a water rat doesn't make a sailor.

He signed up for singing classes with Bobby Cortés, a Puerto Rican who owned his own school in El Barrio. He bought theater clothing and patent leather shoes for dancing the *guarachera*. He spent all his money on that stuff; he didn't drink, he didn't play the numbers, he didn't go to the movies. His was a fixture at Manhattan Center. He liked to go there and dance to Machito's Orchestra and the Afro-Cuban Boys. Every day he made new friends. Most of them were from El Barrio. He joined church choirs thinking that would get him somewhere. He wanted to be an Eddie Cantor or a Cuban Al Jolson, but language and color got in the way. You couldn't even sit in the box seats at Radio City. They were only for whites. A black man there was unthinkable.

Miguelito was the only gray black man in Manhattan. Not only because of the cold, but also because he started to put whitening powder on his face. But that didn't even work. The theater mafia controlled everything and in the end they would choose a black American over a Cuban one.

Bobby Cortés told us stories about how they exploited him and his songs. He'd compose a tune and take it to a radio station or a Latino band. If it was good, the band played it and copyrighted it in Washington. But not in Bobby's name, rather under someone else's name. That's how they stole so many songs, guarachas and boleros. They cheated him big time because he was a pretty honest guy and not a crook.

I went with Bobby and Miguelito to many Latino parties in Jackson Heights, on the Lower East Side and in El Barrio. I mingled with the Boricuas, the biggest Latino group and the friendliest towards Cubans. Miguelito immediately hooked up with a Puerto Rican, although he still sent letters to his woman along with photos of the Empire State Building and the Statue of Liberty. The Puerto Rican woman was very jealous and threatened to rip him apart if he wrote to his woman in Havana. So he wrote the letters from my place and her letters to him came to my address. But the correspondence lessened each time as expected. At first, distance draws people together like a magnet. Over time, though, everything moves to the next level. What's going on in the present gets in the way; people live for today. And inevitably because of something, work, the subway, and a new language, immigrants don't have time to think about their loved ones. That happened to me, too. To be honest, my sister Yara was the only one I ever wrote to.

So, Miguelito eventually got used to things here and soon forgot about his woman. The Puerto Rican woman had him running around all over the place, completely rushed or *ajorado*, as the Puerto Ricans say, and didn't let him get a word in. She had a unibrow, but she was very pretty, although a little uncouth. When he'd go with a bunch of Boricuas to sing at some party, she'd follow.

If he had to work on a weekend at a dance or serenade, she'd follow. She didn't let him out of her sight. That's probably why he forgot about his woman.

"Shit, she doesn't write me anymore!" he told me one day when he saw there was nothing in my mailbox.

"Why would she write you, if you don't even answer her letters?!"

Carmencita had Miguelito wrapped around her finger. They moved in together on the Lower East Side because she got a job in a factory packaging baby clothes. Every day she'd try to make Miguelito jealous: "The foreman tried to touch me" or "The Ecuadorian woman's husband looks at me like this and like that."

"Look, Julián, I really like this woman. I love her, but she's crazy. If she's not acting jealous of me, she tries to provoke me by flirting with other guys."

"Leave her and concentrate on your music."

But he was head over heels in love. Even with all that going on, he still worked a lot; he was really with it. The customers practically threw tips at him because of his good sense of humor. He'd get to the restaurant, after singing his own songs all night in the haunts of El Barrio. Nothing happened to him and everyone spoiled him.

"I dreamt this one up last night," and he'd whip out a score. He wasn't a bad composer; he actually was really musically talented. I could never understand how he could do so many things at once. He wanted nothing more than to make music, but that didn't pay. Musicians worked two jobs because music wasn't enough to make ends meet. He also had to pay for voice lessons and the furniture for the new apartment that cost him an arm and a leg. Miguelito was always with Boricuas, and although he criticized them, he was constantly with them. That way he almost never had to speak English. English classes were too expensive back then. Eventually you learn enough on the street and from newspaper headlines.

Carmencita's sister had come from Ponce a few years back. She brought her six kids and went on welfare. Her husband stayed in Puerto Rico because there was a warrant out for his arrest in New York. Back then people were starving in Ponce. They looked like skeletons when they arrived here. Carmencita helped her find a room in the Bronx. And she wanted to push her on me. She was olive-skinned and quite charming, but the six kids terrified me. We'd go dancing at Manhattan Center, to Coney Island, and spend a good deal of time at the little lake in Central Park. She'd say to me, "I'll leave my husband for you."

And I tried to convince her that it wasn't a good idea for the sake of her kids and my own piece of mind.

"There's no need to rush."

But Boricua women have a fire inside them. They're hotter than Cuban women. She really had me hooked, but I got out of it on time. Her husband wrote that he was coming in March with a safe-conduct permit. I imagine that he wanted to see his kids. He'd already sent his mother to live here. Jeanette and I went out behind her mother-in-law's back. I kept away but she suspected that something was going on and followed me like a rabbit, but she couldn't catch me. When Jeanette's husband arrived, he went to live with her. They had a second honeymoon, but in the long run it ended in disaster. His dirty business brought him all the way to the Bronx. When they went to arrest him, he had a shootout with the police. He wounded one, and went to serve his prison sentence in the Tombs, New York City's prison.

When his mother and the kids went to sleep, Jeanette took two bottles of Seconal and fell asleep. She never saw the light of day again. Her funeral was the saddest thing I've ever seen in my life. The kids didn't understand a thing and they didn't stop crying. It made Carmencita a little crazy. Luckily Phil Dutch, a lawyer from the Working Class Committee, helped the family with a little money and sent the kids to school. Miguelito and I gave the old lady $40 for the flowers and calls to Ponce. It was a nasty situation. Jeanette's parents couldn't come to the burial. Her husband didn't get permission to leave jail for it. Her friends, Miguelito, old José Díaz, Plácido and I had to take care of everything.

Then Carmencita's religious spirit awakened. She started to hang sacred images on the walls of her apartment and she made offerings of water, flowers, and miracles for the children's wellbeing. It tore her apart to see them unhappy, alone on the streets of the Bronx, with a drug addict father in the Tombs and a mother six feet under. There were no parties for a few months. The bands looked for a singer to replace Miguelito since Carmencita made him mourn her sister's death. She put him in a bind because that money helped run the household.

When Jeanette's husband got out of jail, he got a job varnishing furniture in El Barrio. They say he got off drugs and away from the bad life. His kids were already teenagers and some turned into troublemakers because their grandmother couldn't control them. I went with Miguelito to see him one day to ask for a favor. He didn't want to shake my hand. Miguelito said to him:

"This guy's like a brother to me," but he still didn't say a thing to me. It looked like he was hard to get along with, like most ex-cons. He scornfully said to me: "You and I have to settle things first."

But I never saw him again. I always wondered if Carmencita told him something about my affair with her sister. That's why the African tribe Abakuas don't trust women. Sooner or later, they tell it all. There's even a story about a woman who gets her tongue cut out for revealing the secrets of the tribe. I heard that story on the docks in Havana from the *ñáñigo* dockworkers. All of Havana knows about it.

We never saw each other again. I told Miguelito about it.

"Julián, the man is happy finishing furniture now. Let it go."

But the wheel of fortune kept spinning, and after a few months out of the Tombs, he was locked up again. Luckily, Miguelito and his wife never found out about it. I have always abided by the law. I like to sleep at night.

I stayed at El Liborio, but in May of '52 Miguelito and I got a great deal. It was unusual in this city because business is controlled by the mafia and the well-off white Americans, otherwise known as WASPS. Latinos were called spics then, which was not very favorable. Today a spic is a Hispanic, almost as low as an Indian with a loincloth. Some Latinos think that because they made money or won the lottery, they are equal; but if they go to Lord & Taylor or Bloomingdale's and speak Spanish, people give them a mean look. Or if not, the clerks go right up to them and ask "Can I help you?" so that they stop looking around. Latinos are very curious. They'll go into the big shopping centers just to see what's there, to kill some time, to put on some perfume from the tester or to touch a fabric and say at the top of their lungs: "Oh, my god! Look at this color!"

They don't like that act here. Americans are dry. They cut to the chase. We Hispanics ponder things over. Everything's a big deal to us. Boricuas invented rivalry; they're always at odds. Cubans invented showing off. You can spot a Cuban from a thousand miles away because of their flashy style. Today, they're a little better, but no matter what, we always stand out. There's something positive about that. Cubans are loudmouths and don't shut up for anyone. Americans aren't like that. If money is involved, Americans like to move to the fast beat of the conga. If you mess with them, they'll crush you. That's why I admire Fidel's dignity. He put them in their place.

I always beat around the bush when I tell a story. I can't help it. I'm like my grandmother Juana la Callá, when it comes to that. People would say to her, "Juana, get to the point," but she couldn't because she always liked to make things exciting.

I was going to say something about the business but I got off track. Where to begin? A light bulb went off in José Díaz's head. Cubans always come up with something sooner or later. It wasn't enough for him to just have a small shop, he wanted something more. Small shops were all over El Barrio and 47th Street. So he wanted a large jewelry firm from Miami to represent him. They were Cuban brothers of Jewish origin with a lot of money and good chiselers and artists. He went down to Miami and when he got back, he said to me, "Look, Julián, you'll work in the morning. This way you don't have to leave the restaurant."

I usually spent my mornings sleeping because I went to bed late, but I sacrificed my hours of sleep for this new business. Díaz brought a lot of cufflinks, chains, earrings, rings, signet rings, and pounded gold-link bracelets, which were very stylish at the time. I was on the street with my suitcase by nine in the morning, risking my life on the subway and on the streets of El Barrio. I'd go one day to one area and then someplace else the next, just in case someone was watching me. That's how I went around New York, all the way from Canal Street to up past the Bronx. I looked like a zombie when I'd get to the restaurant. I'd look in the mirror and see the bags under my eyes. I lost like thirty pounds, but I did earn some extra money to buy myself a good refrigerator and a thirteen-inch round-screen Zenith. A Spanish customer from El Liborio offered me a job at Dinty Moore, a fancy restaurant on 46th between Broadway and 5th, but I turned it down. The sky was wide open. I earned commission because I knew how to sell. My legs couldn't stop and walking didn't tire me out. Every day I'd go up five or six floors, knock on a door, open my suitcase, show off the earrings and bracelets, and the Latinos would go nuts. The jewelry design from Miami was more appealing to Latinos than what you'd find in New York. You could tell by visiting the pawnshops: the ones in Florida were very different from those in the north.

"You're selling," José said to me.

"I'm going to sell more," I told him one day.

Latinos go crazy over gold, especially if it's a medal or a bracelet. They're so proud to show off a gold medal. But, gold does nothing for me. I like silver because it's not so flashy. But gold is gold and there's always someone who'll do anything to have it.

I met Cuban musicians from the Bronx who spent everything on a gold medal. They pawned their instruments so they could unbutton their shirt and show off a shiny Our Lady of Charity medal, or a Santa Barbara medal with four rubies. That was the crux of the matter. It was a stroke of genius for José to get those things from Miami. He realized that they were going to be a hit among the New York Hispanics. One day I had an ingenious idea.

While I was sitting in a house on 97th and Lexington showing some brooches to a client, I noticed the altar.

"It looks like you guys follow Saint Lazarus."

"Of course! Every December 17th we have the biggest event in all of New York."

Saint Lazarus was bigger than Niño Valdés. I've never seen anything like this; not even at Méndez's place.

Holy Mother! It was overwhelming!

On my way to the subway with my suitcase in hand, I said to myself: "Caramba, if I bring these people medals of saints with precious stones like the ones in Cuba, it'll be like hitting the lottery."

I got off the subway and went directly to José Díaz's small store. I calmly told him about my idea. I didn't want to get too excited. I wasn't going to fail, but something told me, "This is it, Julián, this is it."

José talked to the Kozer brothers right away and told them about the idea. We looked for prayer cards, statues; went to churches; sent away for samples from Cuba. It was an investment, and they listened to me. In about a month, José started getting the medals. They came in all different sizes, but mostly big ones with clasps, engravings, and precious stones: rubies for Santa Barbara; diamonds and topaz for Our Lady of Charity; and amethysts for Jesus Christ of Nazareth. Julián Mesa's medals brought tremendous joy to the community.

I was about to quit the restaurant, but I came to my senses. What if this thing fails? What if it's only temporary? What if it's a fad? Here it was necessary to think with your head and not with your feet. The jewelry business is for people with money. To buy jewels you need money and we didn't have any. One ounce of gold cost $30, a give-away compared to the price nowadays. A medal could cost anywhere from $60 to $80. Today you can't find one for under $1000 and the goldsmith work is totally different. The Kozer brothers got even richer. José Díaz got some money to expand the small store and have his own workshop. My two legs weren't enough, so I got Miguelito involved.

"Leave those music bands and start selling in the Bronx and Jackson Heights. I'll take care of the rest."

For days, the demand was growing and growing. One of my ideas was finally working, but I was the one who got the short end of the stick. I hardly received any commission. I couldn't even get something for each individual sale because the Kozer brothers were monopolists. After all was said and done, I did the right thing by not leaving the restaurant. Money comes and goes, although for some it stays like the snow did that February—and for others it's like a flurry, it disappears right away.

Miguelito kept working in the restaurant with me, but he'd spend all his earnings writing his songs with some musicians who were charlatans and thieves. They charged him an arm and a leg for each song. Because he'd dream of the songs, he got up every day with another new tune to ruin himself with. The songs were even in English in his dreams. In that case he'd spend twice as much, first to correct the language and then to transcribe each song. He bought himself a white jacket and several corduroy hats. He also changed all the furniture in his house because that meant good luck according to Carmencita. He commissioned a medal of Saint Expedite, the patron saint of gamblers. He wasn't religious, but he was superstitious. And as usual he went around flaunting the medal.

"I'm going to see you on 3rd Avenue pawning your stuff, Miguelito. That woman's going to ruin you."

Soon he got what was coming to him. I saw him broker than ever and even trying to pawn his Saint Expedite medal. But even in the worst of times we had a good time. I wanted to write some letters to Cuba. I got the New York fever. Anyone who has lived here knows what I mean. Since everything is about the future, the hope of being rich, you begin to believe for a minute that there's a heaven. It's a temporary illusion, a type of blindness. I wrote to Yara, and to Eva La Libanesa, and to Ñico. Eva was the first to answer me. I must've sounded like things were going great because

Eva wrote: "Save and invest in the stock market." Her father was a businessman. She gave me good advice but I didn't listen to it. I spent everything in no time. I know I screwed up. In the United States, competition governs the market. And right away 18k-gold medals of saints came gushing out of the woodwork. They were made in Cuba, where the gold was good, and they were sent to distributors all over the country. It was an illegal business. Ours didn't fall apart, but it did suffer a good deal. But we did have our moment of glory.

Every weekend we'd go to Coney Island for fun, to play the slot machines or go on the rides. Almost always. If we felt like it, we'd invite Plácido or some Dominican friend. The other Latinos tended to travel in groups, they're more exclusive. But the Puerto Ricans and Cubans always got along well. In the summer many people went to the New Jersey beaches, to the few where we could go. Almost all the beaches here are for white people. They no longer say, "Do not enter," but they don't need to with the face they make if they see someone who isn't white! I've never been crazy about the beaches in this country. It's the one thing about Cuba that I miss the most.

Having fun in New York is expensive; even the places where you can go for free. That's why the Boricuas stay in their neighborhood playing dominos in the summer or go to the *marketa* to buy a ham and some pigeon peas to make a homemade meal. It's cheaper and more entertaining. You can't always go to a boxing match or a film premiere. That's why the kids are so rowdy in the streets, especially in El Barrio. I've never seen anything like it. Even at dawn the troublemakers go around doing their business. They throw bottles, break windows, get into fights . . . And then there's the marijuana issue. Kids smoking and selling it in the middle of the street. What a disgrace! Before it was cleaner, but you could see this coming.

Boricuas were doomed to fail because they didn't find work. And when you don't work and go around like a bum, you get into trouble. In the summer there are more people fooling around on the street, looking for fights or playing cards ... El Barrio is an ant farm in the summer. I go there a lot because the *marketa* on West Park Avenue has the best Hispanic products and the best food. Even though I look Latino, I always carry some kind of protection because you never know what a drunk or a drug addict will do. Just in case, I carry a weapon and don't let Celia leave my side. I've seen a lot of fights over nothing, one too many bloody noses over something stupid. You go to enter a café and some guy comes out and bumps into your woman and doesn't say "Excuse me," but rather "Motherfucker" or something like it. Then you have to go after him. They do it to pick a fight and in El Barrio no one wants to look like a faggot.

116th is the busiest street. Years ago, a leader of El Barrio had the great idea of naming it after Luis Muñoz Marín, a man who betrayed the people of Puerto Rico. His soul was dirty like his teeth. He was a Governor whose name meant something; however, everyone knows who's really in charge of Puerto Rico. He built hotels and highways, but he left the poor people without work in filthy neighborhoods. That's why the working class is here. El Barrio has just as many stupid Boricuas as San Juan.

My barber is from Ponce. They call him an amateur because he's pro-independence. The discussions you hear there are all over the place. That barbershop is like a mini UN in the heart of El Barrio. Not too long ago he had the Cuban and Puerto Rican flags on a mirror. The customers said, "Look, Man, take that down. Cuba is a communist country." But he didn't touch a thing. And when they really insisted he explained that Cuba and Puerto Rico had the best baseball teams in the Americas. That shut everyone up and he just kept on cutting hair.

There were a billion stories about El Barrio during those years. Every day you'd hear about another robbery, murder, rape, or some other crime. They'd cut anyone's face with a Gem blade. Most people were terrified. In any barbershop, no matter where you are, you always hear all about everything. The old men sat down to talk. They'd get off track about what they were saying, but you'd learn something about a bunch of different things. Since I never went to school, I enjoyed listening to old people talk. That's how I learned most of what I know.

In the barbershop, I found out how the Latino neighborhood was formed. It didn't happen overnight. It took some time. Spanish Harlem, East 96th Street to 125th Street, was a completely Jewish neighborhood. Then it changed, as did many other neighborhoods in the city. It's Hispanic for a while and then it's Middle Eastern. This city has a constant flow of foreigners. It's like a Parcheesi game. El Barrio started to take off in the 20s. Before that, Latinos usually lived in Chelsea, where I still live, in Washington Heights, Brooklyn, Queens . . .

In the barbershop, someone was usually talking about the strikes in San Juan and baseball. Many workers came to New York because they were wanted in Puerto Rico: anarchist tobacco rollers and peasants. Some were arrested when they arrived and accused of a plot to kill President Wilson. They never wanted a liberal Hispanic newspaper here. That's why they arrested Puerto Ricans. The talk of the town was the confiscation of newspapers such as *El Corsario* and the mechanization of the tobacco industry. That caused the uprising of hundreds of little stores throughout El Barrio.

In the early 50s, people still had beat-up furniture. When they were evicted, it was a painful sight to see. They used shopping carts to move to another place, always in El Barrio, of course. You'd see them carrying one or two cots and a rickety chair. In the barbershop, they talked about all of this and about nationalist leaders and benefactors. They also talked about the supportive opportunists that had to do with the government of guys like Montgomery Reilly. People still talk a lot about those political issues. The nationalists hung out in one place, the socialists in another. It was basically chaos or *revolú* as they say. The old people remember a lot about Jesús Colón and Bernardo Vega, the founder of the 1920s newspaper *Gráfico*. According to some, they were spokesmen for rights for Boricuas. What can we say about Vito Marcantonio, Puerto

Ricans' favorite congressman? He was the one who said, "I don't have knives to sharpen, nor family members who'll benefit." It was true. Vito was always in favor of independence of the Island.

El Barrio became full of criminals. Many came in through the back door from Latin American countries. They did their sketchy business and gave the Puerto Ricans a bad reputation. They pushed their way into El Barrio and the Jews and the blacks got out of there and let them do their thing.

El Barrio looked like a circus. It's the same today. Only it's not a happy one. People mill around in the streets because they're unemployed. They go in and out of the bodeguitas, botánicas, and cafés. They walk as though they're lost, staring into space, dressed in rags. It's disturbing to see so many human beings like this. Religion gives them comfort; it's the only thing the poor people have in this country. That's why there are more botánicas in El Barrio than anywhere else—but they don't do well because people don't have any money. When people go there, they buy a fruit of the Seven African Powers, luisa herb or some *amansaguapo* or *rompezaraguey* spray. Cuban Santería introduced this city to herbs they've never heard of before and much more. Every day there are more botánicas all over New York. It's incredible. Even in the *marketa* they now have Cuban herbalists. Between the *barajeros* and the *santeros*, or what would be something like the priests of Santería, they flooded New York. It's a way of making a living just like any other. And of course it doesn't require much physical effort.

In spite of everything, Miguelito and I both thought El Barrio was the most entertaining place in New York. It was appealing to us as Latinos. Besides all the vice and blood, they also held dances and beauty contests among the girls from the countryside back home. I went to a bunch of benefit dances for political organizations and local newspapers. They were in different places, nowhere special; fairly big lofts, where they had some Latino group playing sons, guarachas, danzones, and chachachás.

Cuban and Puerto Rican dance music is very similar. That's why it was easy for us to follow them. There was a group called

Yumurí, another called Cubaney. The most popular was Machito and His Afro-Cuban Boys. They played at a high-life place, or somewhere with a little something extra, like Manhattan Center on 34th and 8th, St. Nicholas Arena, and the Palladium. That was more stylish. Sometimes I went, but I liked the atmosphere of El Barrio better. At Manhattan Center, families would bring food in baskets. They'd make a real picnic there under the theater's roof.

The Arts League also threw popular dances, which tended to be a bit posh. I saw the crowning of Jenny Rivera there. She was a girl from the Peñuelas countryside crowned by the Banana Club of fruit merchants. But the good places were in small joints on 116th or Lexington. There was one every three or four blocks. I remember El Cano, a dive very close to St. Cecilia's Church on Lexington between 105th and 106th. Miguelito, his woman, and I would go out on the town when we had some change in our pockets.

By that time drugs were all over the place. It was bad marijuana: cheap and harmful. It was only smoked discretely, not like now how it's all out in the open. Luckily, I was never a fan of it. There are some who say, "Marijuana isn't bad for you. But alcohol is." I'm not the one to make that decision. For me both create a vice and a person with a vice is only half there. I've seen it all and I'm not afraid of anything in life. I always want to have my eyes open in order to enjoy everything to the fullest and with all five senses.

Vito Marcantonio severely condemned the bad reputation attached to Puerto Ricans in New York. There was a time during the 50s, when they were treated worse than any other national group even though they were US citizens. When an American from Oklahoma got to New York, he was well received; but when a Boricua got there, they slammed the door in his face. They could only get jobs as servants, and that was only in some places. It was like a big filter and very few made it through.

Nothing's changed. That's why nobody forgets about them. And although many sellouts and traitors go to the barbershop, in general, most of the customers are progressive. I've been getting my haircut there for thirty years. The barber and I both went gray at the same time. He's always saying that when he retires, he's going to Ponce to buy himself a little ranch. But he's old enough and he hasn't moved an inch. I can understand him. Why jump out of the frying pan and into the fire? It's not worth it. In Puerto Rico, he has to deal with taxes and the entire family's problems. He's spent a good deal of time thinking about it. That's why he's still cutting hair in New York, although he won't admit it. His son is a Nuyorican, he's never been to Puerto Rico, but he's more Puerto Rican than his father. This happens a lot here. The boy speaks English better than Spanish because he was born in New York. The Nuyoricans go to Puerto Rico when they're twenty-one and make some money. Until then, it only exists in their imagination.

"You Cuban! You're rich, damn it."

Because I've always lived in Chelsea and that's downtown and a stone's throw away from the Village, people think I have it good. I don't go to the Village for anything. It's for rich people and artists. I go to work and on the weekends visit a friend or my wife's family. The closest I get to the Village is when I have work there or go to some party at Our Lady of Guadalupe Church on 14th Street. The masses and novenas there are in Spanish and sometimes Celia gets the urge to go. She's Catholic, so she says; a very unique kind of Catholicism if you ask me. I walk her to the door and while she prays and goes around the church, I take a walk on 14th: a gigantic flea market in the hands of Latinos, Jews, and Arabs. Or I go to La Casa de las Américas and wait for her to have Cuban food for lunch with Cuban friends and old emigrants like myself. La Casa de las Américas is our club, the only form of entertainment for the progressive Cubans here. But I'll talk more about that later.

Now I'm going to tell about when I met my wife. Durango Nieves became a close friend of Miguelito Cuesta's. His father owned a thrift shop on 112th Street, a couple of doors down from the *marketa*. I bought almost all of my clothing there. Thrift shops were an invention of the Jews in this country. Supposedly a Polish man came up with the idea when he was picking up old clothing,

used clothing that the rich put out on the stoops of their buildings. The first thrift shop was next to a Red Cross office. People
left things there for the poor and the Jews picked them up and
sold them.

Durango played the conga drum with Miguelito's band and helped
out in his father's shop. He was a Puerto Rican from Aguadilla, but
Durango was born in El Barrio and he was 100% Nuyorican. The
store was small, but did well. Durango's father was a little cheap.
He paid his son a commission once a month for the pieces he sold
during that month. You could say that it was like piecework. On
Thanksgiving and Christmas, he gave him a bonus and a dinner
bill. That's why Durango, like Miguelito, had to earn some extra
money with the traveling band. I didn't make enough in the restaurant either. I was worse off when the medal business started
collapsing. So I started to use my Cuban way of thinking to come
up with something to do. I thought: "If that guy has a thrift shop
and he's a complete moron, why don't I have my own thing?"

I came up with the idea to rent the space above Durango's father
to sell whatever. I told Miguelito about it and he talked me out
of it. Then I consulted José Díaz and he encouraged me to do it.

"Look, Old Man, with what I'll give you for this space, you'll
definitely have the rent covered."

"Okay, Julián. But you're not going to sell clothing."

I didn't need to do that. They already sold used clothing. I
bought books and cheap perfume instead. I painted the place
green and hung a plastic-letter sign in Spanish: "Free Books and
Perfume." That's how I spent my free time. José lent me forty bucks
to buy a thousand books on natural history, politics, and religion.
A Jewish man on 105th who was moving to Midtown sold them to
me. I took a shopping cart to go pick them up. Some were brand
new. It was with the first thing I put in the place. It was a bazaar.
I made the shelves in a weekend. I put a little table out on the
street with the most beautiful books as samples, and that's how the
business started. No one sold books in El Barrio, but the people

there wanted something to read. The books sold faster than the perfume. Some days I made $9 or $10 without even lifting a finger.

I wasn't going to leave El Liborio, so I got a helper and gave him a commission. That's how I met Celia. I'd open on Sundays. On Thursdays, I'd stay there the entire day because that was my day off. I don't know if it was a Sunday or a Thursday when she appeared. I remember that it snowed quite a bit and Carmencita and Miguelito had brought a lot of gold rings for me to sell. Friends would always show up with any old thing without notice. Old paintings, flowerpots, rackety chairs; I sold all of that there except for clothing, of course. The February snow lasts forever and the front door was completely blocked. I never knew if my helper, a very crafty but hardworking Mexican, was in love with her or not. They knew each other because he yelled to her: "Celia, come up. I have something for you."

She pushed the snow out of the way with her feet. She was used to the cold because she was Nuyorican like Durango. She got up there in a flash. *El Mexica*, as we called him, gave her some rings and introduced her to me.

"Look, Julián, this is the most beautiful thing in El Barrio."

I wanted a Cuban woman. I thought I'd always have a bug in my ear with a woman from another place. I wanted to avoid friction and disgust. Almost all marriages between Hispanics were a disaster; Cuban man marries Cuban woman, Boricua man with Boricua woman, Mexican man with Mexican woman and so on. But I fell in love with Celia. How couldn't I? She had bronze skin and jet black hair. And she was very happy. *El Mexica*, I later found out, had met her at a dance on 116th Street. She put on the rings and ran out of there.

"Look, *México*, let me know when there's one of those dances on 116th."

"There's one this Sunday, Julián."

I got Miguelito and Carmen excited and we went to the Borinquen Club to a benefit dance with the Cuban group Yumurí. I bought myself a red tie in Durango's place and went out knowing

I was going to run into Celia. She was the only thing I thought about. I was obsessed. On the way, Carmencita gave me a slap on the neck.

"So, Julián, you want to fuck that girl. Don't you realize that you are about twenty years older than she is?"

It wasn't true. At eighteen Celia was a real woman. I don't know if I was thirty-five yet, but I was close. That saved me. When I saw her walk into the dance dressed in red, my soul got happy. It was that chill you get throughout your body that makes the manliest man timid. I went over to *El Mexica* and said:

"*Oye, México*, help me out a little, okay?"

"Okay, man," he said to me, "but the *chiquita* is from the countryside."

"No way, she was born here. And she looks like she's on the ball."

"I already introduced you to her, Man."

"Introduce me to her again, *chico*."

El Mexica got his people involved in the business because his commission wasn't enough to put food on the table, but he was very fun. Miguelito let him sing in the band and in one month he learned over twenty boleros, like a good person from Vera Cruz. The dance hall was small and stank like kerosene. The heat cranked up so high and the mix of women's perfumes was enough to make anyone vomit, but the music was delightful. They played a lot of chachachás. They were big back then. "*Vamos al túnel, mi vida, vamos al túnel mi amor . . .*" I bought a Budweiser and sat alone in the corner. *El Mexica* was getting silly with one of Celia's friends. I stayed seated watching her walk around that little hall, not dancing with anyone. Everything she did amused me, I liked everything. I was crazy about her; my jaw dropped just looking at her.

Many Puerto Ricans born here speak Spanish with a special accent. Once in a while they insert words in English. When they bump into someone they say, "Excuse me" and not "*Perdón*." And when they get all worked up they scream in English, using curse words. It's typical of Nuyoricans. The majority feels more Puerto Rican than North American and that was the case with Celia. But since she lived in El Barrio, she had Boricua customs; she dressed, ate, did everything thing like a Latina. That's why I liked her so much. However, she'd never been to Puerto Rico. And she talked about her country, well, her parents' country, like a Cuban talks about Cuba, or a Mexican talks about Mexico. I would've preferred a Cuban woman, but today, after thirty years of marriage, I don't regret it, because Celia is like gold to me.

I went to get her to dance with me.

"I don't know how to dance Cuban-style," she told me a little embarrassed.

"But everyone dances it, Girl."

"No, you Cubans are the ones who know how to dance it."

We started to laugh. When you fall in love, everything makes you laugh. You talk about the stupidest things in the world. You are careless, you let loose. We didn't even dance once that night. We didn't pay attention to the snacks or the sweets. I drank about ten beers and my tongue got completely tangled. She drank a little. She sometimes answered me in English. She lived with her aunt who told her that men appear to be gentle like lambs but they have a snake's tail, with poison to harm women.

"My aunt is more like a mother to me," she told me.

We didn't dance, but we spent the entire night together. The next day in the café Celia's voice was ringing in my ear. I tried to picture her face and I couldn't. I don't know how I could function at work. I don't know how I could be days without seeing her. I went to look for her in El Barrio and had no luck. She'd gone with her aunt to the Bronx to her goddaughter's baptism. She was there for a few days.

"When you see her, call me right away at the restaurant."

El Mexica called me and I got there in a flash. I spent the day's tips on a taxi. It was the first one I took in my entire life in this city. I made it to El Barrio in twenty minutes. I grabbed a perfume from the store, put it in my pocket and started to look for her all over 112th. It was useless. I went all over that part of El Barrio. I went to her house and her aunt told me, "She's always out and about."

I went back to the store and as I was going up the stairs, I heard Celia's voice.

"You got here just in time, Julián," *El Mexica* said to me.

I don't believe in saints, but I do believe in miracles. I'm pretty lucky. She had gone there to look for me, to talk to me. When I put my hand in my pocket to give her the perfume, she said to me, "I'd like to get some kind of job. Could you help me?" I gave her the perfume and stared at her.

"Forget about that for now. We're going to talk a little." There was slave work in the factories, but it was a job for machines, not for a woman like Celia. The factories were prisons. The floor ladies, as they're called, were like military leaders. They were dykes and tyrants. When a worker wanted to go to the bathroom, she had to raise her hand like you did back in school. They were known to beat their employees.

"Back, to work," they'd scream in English when the women would get distracted for some reason or fall asleep.

I couldn't imagine a woman as delicate as Celia in a factory. That's why I talked her out of it. Her aunt lived on welfare and took care of Celia's little brothers and sisters. There were times when no one worked and sometimes their stomachs touched their spines.

There's a novel inside each of us. My wife's story was sad, even sadder than mine. I left my house, went to Havana, found work, came here, and now I'm in a country that I've never liked. But everything that I've done was because of my own will, all because I got some idea in my head. When I met Celia, she was an orphan and didn't have a plan. Her life was like a soap opera. Life is stranger than fiction. I haven't read many novels, I haven't had the time; I bought them to sell, not to read. But I've sucked the juice out of life. As a Chinese philosopher once said, the book of life is infinite. If people would only talk to their pillow a little more, but they live for today and don't think enough. They want to earn money, lose weight, buy a house or an ounce of dope. But very few people really think. If I'd planned things better before complicating my life here, I would've gone to live in Cuba in 1959. But what's done is done.

My wife's story is sad as I was saying earlier. That's why I married her right away.

"You're the man. You decide."

"Tomorrow," I said.

Miguelito and the others helped me. I needed two witnesses so I called José Díaz and Plácido. Miguelito was like my brother so I didn't have to get along well with him. She asked Durango's parents and we went to City Hall and before we knew it we came out husband and wife. We were both so happy! It's obvious in the pictures that we took at Battery Place, with all those little flowers in the background. Especially in this one, the date's on the back: March 12, 1953. Batista was already doing his thing.

Since she was an American citizen, I went to see a lawyer and he got me residency in a flash. That granted me a more defined status in this country, but I didn't make more money, nor did it make me happier. Celia has been the perfect wife. She reminds me of Emerlina a bit, although I can't put my finger on why exactly. Puerto Ricans are very noble, and that's how she is. I think she gets it from her father because her mother took off one day, a little before dying of a bad illness.

Celia's mother was from San Juan, from a very poor area of town. A man brought her as a very young girl to New York and left her on the street. Then she got together with Benjamín, Celia's father. Supposedly he was a very hardworking man and they had four children. In order to support them, he went to work for a North American company in Panama. He'd send them money. But one day he was killed in a brawl and Celia's mother set her hair on fire and burned it all instead of slitting her wrists. Celia was about eight at the time and her sisters and brothers were even younger. The poor thing remembers very ugly things. Just to give you an example, when Celia was young and would ask for food, her aunt would throw them beans on a plate and say, "Lick this so you won't be hungry." She takes care of us now because she's old and I still help out the kids.

You don't forget things like that. Especially when the mother left for good. It hit her like a rock. That's why Celia forgives her aunt and loves her very much. She was left alone with a lot to deal with.

"Esperanza, take care of the kids for me, I'm going to look for some guys. I'll be right back."

She got together with an older man and that was it. Then they received the news that she died with bruises all over her body in a clinic in Queens.

Esperanza lives alone. She's into that *espiritismo* stuff. She has a room full of images of saints. She sells prayer cards and reads palms and the bottoms of people's feet. She has the Holy Child of Atocha and Santa Martha painted on the door of her house on 106th and Lexington. We go there when she asks for something to make her happy, because my wife is very grateful for her despite everything. But she tells us that the spirits come at night to steal money from the hem of her nightgown. And that's when I get fed up with her and ask her the question that drives her crazy: "Esperanza, why would the dead want money?" When we say goodbye, she goes and throws a glass of water in the toilet to get rid of the "bad spirits." I married Celia because of all this and took her to Chelsea right away.

We had our honeymoon at home. We spent less and had more fun. Soon after, we went on a trip with Miguelito and Carmen to the Jersey beaches, but it wasn't a honeymoon. Celia put artificial flowers and ceramic decorations all over my place. My life completely changed. I never again sewed a button or did the dishes. I have the perfect wife, that's for sure. The only obstacle has been Wenceslao, something her aunt came up with. It must've been before the wedding. Celia got some strange idea. Everything was Wenceslao this and Wenceslao that . . . until one day.

When I got home I wasn't in the best mood. I found the aunt giving advice to Celia on behalf of some Wenceslao.

"Child, remember that Wenceslao has prohibited you from having more than two people over at a time."

"Come here. Who's this Wenceslao?"

But it was impossible. I'm not even that social. Once in a while I like to invite someone over to have a coffee or to talk a little about stupid things, but there was no way around it. Wenceslao ruled in my house.

"Celia, you-know-who says that you shouldn't . . ."

They no longer said the name. It was now "you-know-who." I got fed up with it, because you eventually get fed up with everything. Besides that, I'd never heard Celia ever mention that name.

"If I hear you talking about this Wenceslao again, I'm leaving! And I won't be back!"

That's how it happened. I don't know how they arranged it, but Wenceslao got lost. Who's ever heard of a guardian prohibit a woman from sleeping with her husband? That's how bad it got!

I sold my last two medals. I sold one of the Virgin of Guadalupe to a co-worker of mine, *El Mexica*, and the other to a Chinese man. It had a dragon and two rubies on it. He owned a deli on 6th Avenue. The Chinese man fell in love with the medal, something that only they can understand, and he paid me cash for it. I would've never sold it to him because Chinese people are very strange. Chinatown is the only neighborhood in New York where I never go. It's another world over there. And if you ask for directions, you're screwed. They always answer, "Don't know." One day I was looking for a bakery and I asked a Chinese man in English.

"Hey, Sir, do you know where Sweet Dove Bakery is?"

"I no know bakery," he answered walking away from me.

But what comes around goes around. A few days later I got even when on 23rd Street a Chinese man asked me, "Train downtown, please?"

"*En la casa de carajo,*" I screamed at him in Spanish just like that, walking away from him.

Here you can't give up your seat on the train, nor can you take a blind person by the hand. First you must ask them if they want help. People get offended. It's not like that in Cuba, good manners in this city are different. The rules aren't the same. I haven't gotten used to it. Cubans do not conform very easily like other immigrants, I'd say. They don't forget about where they came from. If there's a Cuban restaurant, it's packed with Cubans. If there's a Hispanic film playing, Cubans go see it. If a Latin American theater company or a Spanish repertoire comes to town, Cubans don't miss it. Cubans don't forget about their country. I sometimes talk about Cuba and it's as if I were there. I don't know, I feel in my element with Cubans. That's why I don't leave La Casa de las Américas. We play dominos, watch films, talk about politics, and eat real Cuban food. My wife and I celebrate New Year's Eve there: it's the closest we can get to Cuba. Even though she was born here, she loves Cuba as if it were her own from hearing me talk about it all the time.

Boricuas are pretty much the same. Even those born here feel Puerto Rican. They are kind of reserved at first. Puerto Ricans don't easily trust anyone, they think a lot before getting close to someone. And they have a point. Puerto Rico's history is very sad, one pirate after another seizing their treasures. So why would they trust anyone? Friendship takes time with them. There are differences, although we're both very similar kinds of people. A Puerto Rican grandmother is a saint. The world could end, but they still respect her. That's why in El Barrio, despite everything, it's pretty safe for Boricuas. Who's going to rob your house if your grandmother lives there? Who's going to get your grandmother involved with drugs or a crime? No one. Grandmothers are like fortresses. That's how it was back in the neighborhoods of Jesús María and Atarés! We're a very similar race, don't you think?

It would've been great to have Celia stay at home, but the jewelry business fell apart and I let *El Mexica* go. Everything happens for a reason. He was already doing something that wasn't right in there. He looked like shit from head to toe. He brought bums to my place, parasites, etc . . . They went there to hang out or to warm up in the corner. That fun, noble boy I once knew turned into a real player. He turned bad. He couldn't even sing in the bands because he was always drunk. The funniest thing of all was when I told him, in a nice way, "Look, Man, I'll give you $20 and we're even."

He answered, "I'm not leaving. Half of this belongs to me."

He did collect some books on the street and bring them there, but I told him, "I'll give them all back to you. Take them."

He didn't do a thing, he didn't listen. But he did listen to his buddies' advice and got a lawyer. The lawyer came to ask me for the tax certificate. I put all the papers on the table for him. The Mexican's name didn't appear anywhere. The lawyer got the hell out of there begging me for forgiveness and scared that they were going to slash his stomach in El Barrio. He looked more like a jerk than a lawyer. The following Sunday *El Mexica* came to see me in the small store. I was there with Celia straightening things up when I heard, "Julián, you want to send me to the Tombs."

I stopped dead in my tracks, "Get your books and get out of here."

He started to cry. He was half drunk and started to complain to me about Miguelito. He was a hideous human being. I've seen men turn into total losers, but never to the degree to which that poor guy did.

After two or three months Durango came to tell me, "They arrested *El Mexica*. It was drugs. He's in the Tombs."

My wife looked at me with that look in her eyes that says "this was bound to happen."

Celia knew English inside out. She could read the titles of the books, while I didn't even pay attention to them. I simply priced them and that was all! But she didn't work that way. She put them in order by content, put covers on some, and then started to buy fantasy fiction from Chinatown and Church Street to sell in our small store. After a few months of being busy with the business, when things got a little better, she became pregnant. We both wanted a child, but we didn't mean for it to happen so unexpectedly. Miguelito offered to take care of the shop for me because with the music thing, he couldn't make ends meet. I didn't want him to think that I didn't trust him, so I agreed. The two of us still worked at the restaurant. If it had to be between a factory and El Liborio, we picked El Liborio.

Celia gave birth to a nine-pound baby girl just like her but with darker skin. We named her Yara after my sister. My wife liked the name since the first time she heard me say it. My sister answered the letter in which I proudly told her about what'd been going on recently. She asked me for pictures of the wedding and of the baby girl. Celia and I were very happy. On summer Sundays, we'd go to Central Park to look at the trees and the little lakes, and to people-watch. Some bands like Benny Goodman played the popular songs of the time out in the open air. The trumpet became as popular as the guitar. Riding the bus was also quite entertaining. We took the one on 6th and 19th Street and made our way uptown, distracted by all there was to see. If not, we'd get together with Carmencita and Miguelito and prepare a very typical Cuban meal, of what we call *mofongo*, colored beans, and *tembleque*, coconut flan, for dessert with Cuban coffee.

This is worth telling. One day a musician from an American band came to eat with us. When he saw the *mofongo*, he asked, "What's this?"

Miguelito answered him in English, totally convinced that he'd understand: "It's a kind of *fufu*."

The guy asked him, "What's *fufu*?"

Miguelito said, "It's a sort of *mofongo*."

You couldn't explain it. That's how we'd spend a good amount of time. But everything wasn't rose colored. The child brought us expenses and other responsibilities. I closed the shop in El Barrio. Celia couldn't take care of it and I wasn't going to leave my job as a waiter in a restaurant where I'd been for several years. However, a little beanstalk fell from the sky for me. Plácido reserved an apartment for me on the third floor with better conditions, a full bathroom, a kitchen, and a room for the child. I bettered my situation thanks to the time I spent in El Barrio and to Plácido, a fellow Cuban. Today this house where I live could rent for $600 or $700 depending on what the owners feel like asking. They've given it to me for $190 because of rent control. If not, I'd be screwed because New York rent payments are higher than the buildings. It's a costly abuse.

Today everything seems to be out of control. That's why I feel very let down. When I arrived I had many ideas, but they didn't completely work out. I'm not saying that other Cubans haven't achieved their dreams. Anything is possible in New York. Some made money, that's for sure, from their career or drugs. They bought themselves a house in Queens or Union City after having worked 12-hour days. They've lived outside of Cuba for more than half their lives and they can't understand their children who were born here because they're Americans. And most of the time the children have completely different customs than their parents. I didn't want that life for me. It wasn't what I dreamed of, but it happened because at times you are like a top that spins round and round without knowing where you'll stop.

An emigrant's life is the most solitary in the world. I'm not saying anything bad about the North Americans; they're very hardworking and independent people. They don't go getting involved with the lives of others. But it's something else. North Americans could be carrying a suitcase full of bills and no one would ever know. Hispanics would brag about it right away to the first person they'd see. Hispanics are more open, more straight-forward. North Americans live in their houses, Hispanics live in El Barrio dancing or playing dominos on the sidewalk with the music from the boom box blasting. Hispanics have a toothache and everyone knows about it. North Americans don't tell anybody. They simply go to the dentist when they have the money. My wife spends everything on aspirin.

"Oh shit! Oh my god!" she complains in English.

I tell her in Spanish, "Go to the dentist, Dear."

There's nothing worse than a toothache. But it's impossible with her. She answers me, "It's my nerves, Julián." So I take her to the psychiatrist. They check her from head to toe. They charge me an arm and a leg and the diagnosis is always the same, "A nervous breakdown, Sir. That'll be $50 for today." The last time the same doctor offered a possible solution: "Tell your wife to eliminate anything that can be harmful to her." I decided to eliminate the doctor.

Hispanics cure themselves with lime tree and aspirin. Psychiatrists are for rich people. And for people who have nothing better to do. In this city, you have to be careful because anyone can fall off the deep end. There's a lot of commotion, a lot of noise, lots of smog, lots of fear. It's dangerous to go out at night. You don't dare to cross Washington Square Park after midnight. And it's in a nice neighborhood. You don't dare to sit in Union Square or Central Park. This city has many attractions, that's for sure. For some it's the center of the world. The Big Apple as they call it. But it's necessary to take care of it. I've seen how it has swallowed up innocent people who arrived here when they were young to look for a job and didn't want to get involved with gambling or drugs. Their head was in one place and one of the many tentacles of the city sucked them to another. New York is an octopus.

"More was lost in the war, Julián."

But I couldn't get used to it. I had lost the shop. And if King Farouk abdicated or not, I didn't give a damn. I still wanted to hold my head high. I didn't let my arm be twisted. Cubans are like that. She wasn't. She was obedient, a conformist. Our little girl became the center of her world. And there wasn't enough money coming in. King Farouk was a fat slob. He left millions behind and I didn't even have a place to die. As my grandmother would say, "We poor don't die." There was nothing else I could do, but to keep going.

I didn't buy a newspaper for months. The stupid things they talked about only made me sick. Everything was "So-and-so Arrives in Washington," "The First Lady Hosts Dinner for This and That Person," or "So-and-So Injured Jumping Out of a Plane in Mount Grove." Bullshit is what they call it here, or as we Cubans like to say *"cacafuaca."* The only acceptable newspaper was *The New York Times*. You need good English to read the *Times*, especially to understand the headlines. Here, Hispanics read *El Diario de Nueva York* or *La Prensa*. They were more or less pro-government, partially yellow journalism. Now they've merged into one: *El Diario de la Prensa*. Same shit, different day. When the Korea War was at its height, they published whatever they wanted. Of course the Americans won. Every day the artillery and allied tanks made meat of the reds. They'd describe mountains covered with dead bodies; a total desolation in the south, desertions. It was the same story later in Vietnam: one lie after another. But it was the only newspaper in Spanish during those years. As they like to say here "No choice."

The White House paid more attention to Truman and Somoza than to the armistice signing between the allies and communists. It was scandalous. You didn't need a college education to see what was really going on. The nation turned upside down during the Korean War: thousands of Colombians, Puerto Ricans, Cubans, and blacks were falling like flies; a steel crisis like never before; more than 600,000 workers on strike; and the government trying to get out of the situation by announcing new posts and elections. Evita Perón's death was all over the place. People really felt it. They had several masses at St. Patrick's Cathedral and Our Lady of Guadalupe Church. It was over the top. Although, it's true that Perón was in favor of the working class at that time. Perhaps that's why they made a fuss about her here.

We Hispanics are practically invisible. We don't have a voice or vote. Malpractices and outrages were the order of the day. We felt totally neglected. It wasn't all about getting rich, you wanted to be part of it all, and there was no way to do so. That's why after a few years, Hispanics give up and isolate themselves. In poor neighborhoods, for example, no one shovels the snow. There are no plough trucks, nothing. If you don't go out with salt and break your back shoveling, you have to stay trapped in the house. The city didn't give a damn.

I remember in Brooklyn a friend of Carmencita's godmother, Emilio Morfi, had his house destroyed because one day he ran out screaming, "Gas, gas!" Drops of gas were coming out of some crack, but it wasn't an oilfield or anything like it. After that, Emilio was homeless for several months. He made appeals to the county so that they'd rebuild his house, but nothing happened. He formed a coalition of the willing. That's how he built it up again. If I told you it was any other way, I'd be telling a lie.

For all the compassion that you feel for humanity, when you lose everything and have a child to feed, you bear the weight of the world on your back. My wife was going around saying "More was lost in the war" and I was trying to figure out how to pay the bills because a curse had fallen on me.

Miguelito moved to Red Hook, a Puerto Rican neighborhood in Brooklyn. There he started to work for some of Carmencita's relatives. He worked for a while as a mechanic; he'd take cars apart and then sell the pieces. An odd business. Celia got all excited because she was in her element there. She wanted to move to Brooklyn, but I wouldn't stand for it. Red Hook was a very bad neighborhood, like Los Sures. You saw everything there.

"Last night I had a dream about a dog, Julián."

"Great. What's that supposed to mean?"

"That we're going to move and have money."

But neither happened. We entertained ourselves by going to visit our friends on Sundays. Red Hook is something like El Barrio, but even more neglected. Sure, the rent was cheap, but it was hell on earth.

The same day of the ceasefire when the armistice was signed in Panmujon, a photo of Batista along with the news about the attack on the Moncada headquarters was in the papers. It was July 27, 1953. That night we said goodbye to Miguelito at his house in Brooklyn. He wanted to join the Merchant Marines and be a cook on a ship called the *American*. I didn't have the will to sign up as a marine. The union would've accepted me, but I didn't have the globetrotter spirit that Miguelito had. I think that underneath it all, I'm just a *guajiro* going around with little ambition. He's got it though: he's a stray bullet. Even during the worst of times, his spirits are up. When they took away his house on Avenue C on the Lower East Side and left him without a pot to pee in, he said to me, "Julián, I'm moving to Brooklyn."

He said it with the all happiness and optimism of someone who has just hit the lottery. He's one in a million. Then he told me about Ornato Studios, an academy in Brooklyn . . .

It's nothing, Julián. I went there to introduce myself. Since all the doors already closed in my face, I figured I had nothing to lose. So I gave Ornato Studios a try. I asked for an interview and they gave it to me, but when I got there they said to me, "Your accent is very strong. It's very noticeable." That was it. That's why I'm moving to Brooklyn. And no more restaurants, I no longer serve anyone else. Now I'm in the business of buying and selling car parts. It pays more and I don't have to answer to anyone. Be excited for me, will you?!

He wanted to drag me to Red Hook with him, but I refused to go. I had a good head on my shoulders. I didn't want to be a William Fox or a Desi Arnaz. Maybe they did begin pressing pants or waiting tables, but they were lucky. There's something, something big, that's called a star, and not everybody can be one.

He wasn't in the mechanic business for long because he immediately got involved with working on the ships through some of José Díaz's friends. They were socialists and long-time members of the Mella Club. Many of them had gone to fight in the Lincoln Brigade during the Spanish Civil War. They controlled the National Maritime Union. Get close to a good tree, and you'll have good shade.

It went well for Miguelito on the ships, but his wife, a total Boricua, got more and more jealous. She was making herself sick. Her godmother, with her prayers and potions, almost pushed her off the deep end. On the day Jorge Negrete died, Carmencita put a black belt in her hair and refused to eat. Miguelito was lost in the middle of the ocean. His absence ate away at her. We'd go there and she'd complain about everything. Celia didn't like Red Hook because even at night in the summer, it was like a ghost town. The train's whistle was the only sign of life. But Carmencita was alone and Miguelito had left me in charge of going to see her while he was out at sea.

It was a hassle to get to Red Hook back then. Now it's worse because of the drugs and gambling that go on there. But in the 50s that was the closest thing to El Barrio. I always remember the words of a Boricua politician during a meeting at Manhattan Center, "Latin America starts in New York." And it's true. The Latino streets of Brooklyn are anthills, especially in Red Hook and Los Sures. Miguelito was in his element there. Drums, rumbas, Boricua bombas, chachachás everywhere.

Today it's the same with the Pentecostal hallelujah choirs and the salsa groups, or the young kids dancing to music. They have break dance here: pure acrobatics, moves for the young and flexible. That's what it was like in the Brooklyn neighborhoods. The same kids who were responsible for decorating the subway with graffiti also painted a bunch of crosses on the streets. Red Hook and Los Sures were known for having a life of luxury, unlike other areas of New York. It's very difficult for these people to find a job. So they start stealing cars and taking them apart piece by piece. They sell the parts until the police catch them off-guard and that's when they start to regret it. The hallelujah choirs with their drums, clarinets, and guitars, spend the entire day singing salvation songs for the deviant spirits. But that doesn't get rid of hunger and other basic needs.

Every day there are more and more crosses with Puerto Rican flags painted on the streets and walls of Red Hook and Los Sures. Someone goes down because he's shot or stabbed and they paint a cross to remember him. It gives them the necessary comfort to go on with life. It was always like this in the Latino neighborhoods. On the cross they put the initials R.I.P. (which here means Rest in Peace). For some people it really means *República Independiente de Puerto Rico*.

Since there's no work, most families are on welfare and food stamps, especially the families with a lot of kids. And they spend their money on the most incredible things. If a Latino gets married, he spends it all in the blink of an eye. He rents a black Cadillac with a chauffer in cap and uniform for the wedding, fills his house with flowers, and buys an obscene amount of rum although it tastes like rat poison or *pitorrio*, as the Boricuas would say. If they have enough money, they rent St. Nicholas Arena or the Palladium and throw a three- to four-hour dance without missing one single detail. That's the good thing about Latinos, money is for spending and not for investing.

When Latinos have a little extra money in their pocket, their first stop is the butcher. A butcher, not a nylon or cellophane laboratory like the American delis. A butcher shop with live game and fresh meat, nothing frozen. Jerked beef, pig legs, feet, tripe. That's what we're used to. Or they go to the cinema, *el meadito*, whatever they call it, but it's basically a movie theater.

Back then Hispanic cinemas were everywhere. Now they're nowhere to be found. They don't put them in the *New York Magazine* or the movie guides because they don't count. But sometimes they show good movies. I still go to a *meadito* on 107th to see movies from my time. My wife is a fan of Mexican movies. Every once in a while they show *La hija del penal* with María Antonieta Pons and *Gallo en corral ajeno* with Jorge Negrete and Gloria Marín. I like those Mexican movies a lot. They also show them on the Hispanic TV channels. Since television back then wasn't anything like it is now, you'd go to the movies more often. I remember they sold peanut candy, natural coconut ice cream, and *cuchifritos*, Puerto Rican fried food. We went several times with Miguelito to the Puerto Rico Theater on 138th and Brooklyn Avenue. Celebrities like Carlos Ramírez, the Colombian baritone, Mirta Silva, Daniel Santos, and Ninón Sevilla, the most famous Cuban woman of Mexican film, sang there.

Today most young people spend everything on video games, gadgets, and drugs. It's a shame because they miss out on the little pleasures in life. That's one of the reasons why people aren't that close. Before, everyone seemed to have a common understanding. Friendships were more solid. They were more meaningful. Drugs also have a lot to do with it. They make people selfish. They make them lose their mind little by little. That hurried, *roshada*, way of walking on the street is a drug in and of itself sometimes.

What saves Puerto Ricans is the support from their families, solidarity. My wife taught me that. "Your family never lets you down," they say. Puerto Rican families are like Cuban families and then some. The most distant cousin is considered a relative, and if they can, they'll help you out. You see it in their neighborhoods. Three people eat from one plate of beans and that's that. If you can't count on your family, then who can you count on? The social workers say, "Stay close, because if you look for support in the system, you're fucked." They give alms to survive. But work is the most important thing. It's what they really need. It's what Latinos yearn for most and there hasn't been any. The other day a little old lady, who was about ninety, showed me a photo of herself and Albizu Campos and said to me, "There I have a 45 pistol. That's how it was in my time, and that's how it should be now."

Carmencita's poor state was partially due to her husband's absence. She was completely out of it. My wife couldn't do anything about it. When a person loses their mind and thinks that religion will save them without looking at the bigger picture, they're helpless. That's what happened to her. And her godmother came to make bad things worse. I can't explain Carmencita's behavior. I've never been able to explain it. She was really attached to Miguelito and when a Puerto Rican is really taken by a man, it's worse than a barnacle stuck to a shell. There isn't anything that can change their minds. It crippled her. And she didn't even want to see the light of day. When we'd go visit her, we'd see unopened letters from Miguelito on the kitchen table. They were endearing letters that she never read. She was no longer interested in anything that had to do with life. Not even our daughter could make her crack a smile. Miguelito told about the fun he was having on the ships, the countries where he docked, the parties in the kitchen where he was the lead singer. She didn't even bother to read the letters. If I didn't go there . . .

"Look, Julián. Read them. Find out what my husband's up to."

I opened the letters and read to her:

Dear Chinita,

Yesterday we docked in Bergen. It's very cold, more so than there in New York. But luckily the first aid officer lent us thick coats. There are a lot of people in this port. They sell live fish in enormous wooden barrels. Chinita, the rivers are like canals that lead to an ice wall. Bergen is full of fjords. Almost all the Norwegian seamen have a beard to protect themselves from the cold. I miss you very much. I spend every night writing songs for you. We're sailing to Liverpool from here on the 13th. I have eleven more days left working totally enclosed, the worst part, but that's how I get the most overtime. Write me and let me know how everyone's doing over there. Take care of yourself and don't forget about me.

I love you,
Miguelito

Or he'd tell her about the adventures of the *Flight Enterprise*. It was a cargo ship filled with supplies of food and water that made a trip to Japan at the end of the Korean War when people got on boats to change their lives. The *Flight Enterprise* wasn't a luxury ship like the *America* or the *Constitution*. It was a freighter. It also carried jeeps and trucks. When it docked in some port, the people working on the docks would ask the crew members for cigarettes, wristwatches, and record player pieces in exchange for typical souvenirs. The attendant, as he was called, gave the seamen a ration of six packs of cigarettes for less than $10 and the seamen sold the packs for $5 each. The money would flow in. When Miguelito got back he told us that Europe was very poor during those years. People by the ports would go through the dumpsters every day to pick up the coffee dregs they'd throw out. They'd ask them for gum and old clothes. He felt like a millionaire looking at those towns destroyed by World War II. The stories about life at sea were terrible, but much more interesting than the ones about the restaurant. That's why I didn't miss a letter. And when I more or less suspected that he was about to arrive, I bought *La Prensa* to read the *Notas del Puerto* on page two. That's where they put the arrival of boats at the New York docks.

The stories were fantastic. I still can't believe some of them. One was about Miguelito's marine friend named Marcel Milliard, or Marsellés. He was completely crazy. He paid fifteen thousand francs for permission from the court in Marseille to tattoo his wife from head to toe and pull all her teeth out. They're things that being out at sea does to you. Miguelito became an expert cook and first-class marine. The people on the boats loved him like crazy. He'd spend the whole time singing, dancing, and fucking around.

He became crippled because of a lousy deckhand. He was a Colombian guy who challenged him to jump from one pole to another holding on to a cargo rope.

"Grab it. It doesn't have thorns!"

They competed against each other. They did this in front of the crew, as if it were a show. The skin slid off the palms of his hands and he fell on the edge to the entrance to one of the holds. He fractured his leg in three places and couldn't get a cast. He walked on it for about two or three days. When he arrived at the port, his leg was useless and it never went back to normal. It's an occupational hazard with a primitive cure.

In Brooklyn they called him "Stick leg" because he walked like the pirates do in the movies, but it didn't bother him. He made it to New York and tried to cheer up his wife. He took her out of the house when he could, but she didn't do a thing. She was completely out of it. Miguelito couldn't continue on the ships. He was crippled for life, furthermore, the big ships like *America*, *Independent*, and *Constitution* were out of style. The airplane took over the transatlantic ship market. Robert McNamara did all kinds of tricks to get rid of the ships and he was successful. Even with the many union protests, and marches in Washington, nothing could be done. The airplane appeared overnight and immediately became a hit. The ship for long trips became a thing of the past. Freighters were very risky and only dealt with black market stuff. Miguelito's plan backfired on him. He couldn't even get a job at the marina because he didn't have more than five years of experience at sea. He went back to the restaurants part-time and to selling junk on 23rd Street.

In order to get ahead in this city it's necessary to have good contacts and a tough set of balls. Even then the party doesn't last for long. It was depressing to see Carmencita. She'd gone half crazy. Miguelito didn't want to recognize it. He'd dealt with her for more than ten years; with her and her godmother because he'd practically married both of them. On top of that, her godmother was just like Esperanza and she moved to Red Hook with her practice and everything. She took Carmencita to the hallelujah concerts in the parks, smeared her with ointments from the botánica and covered her with protection. She blamed it all on Miguelito. She called Celia on the phone and told her horrible stories about me, downright inventions. Luckily, my wife doesn't listen to what people say. If she did, it would've destroyed our marriage. That witch worked in vain. She didn't even cure Carmencita. She couldn't turn Celia against me. She hated people. "The earth is a valley of tears." And she blamed it all on men. She raised slanders. Insulted people because she liked it. However, her practice was full of women. She was a viper with a halo. She cast spells with Holy Mary oil and her phony prayers. Miguelito's house was full of candles. Everything for her godmother, because he . . . He'd seen so many stupid things in his life!

The woman decorated the Sacred Heart altar with green, black, yellow, seven-color candles . . .

"There's nothing I can do, Julián. There's a curse on this woman."

We stopped going because it wasn't worth it. And I didn't want to have much to do with it all in case it would rub off on Celia. There were already signs.

One night I get home from the café and I find Celia lighting some black candles.

"They're to get rid of the bad spirits, Julián."

I kept my mouth shut. But when I go in the bathroom to put back the sprays, I find two green candles and two seven-color ones on the shelf.

"Don't touch that, Julián. You'll see how things are going to get better for us. The green candles are for money and the others to see if we can go on a little trip."

I kept my mouth shut again. One day things got out of hand and the place looked like a botánica instead of a house. I took the candles and the bottles of Florida water and threw them down the trash chute. Church was over! There was crying as expected. The next day we won $41 on the lottery. It was a little spark, but mostly it was a lesson. "Thank goodness!" I said to myself. I already had enough with what was going on with Miguelito to have to deal with the same thing in my own house. And I had my daughter to deal with.

"Damn it, Julián. It's proof that it works."

"Of course it is."

But that altar was gone for good. She does get her fix once in a while though. She cleans with Florida water, but the candles and plaster saints look best in the botánicas where they belong.

After battling a lot with Carmencita, there was nothing left to do but check her into King's County Hospital in Brooklyn. Getting her a spot in there was a headache. But we did get one once she was a human waste. The mentally ill still mill around the streets of New York. According to the census, there are more than sixty thousand who aren't medicated in rooms, hotels, and subway stations. You see it everywhere you go. It's not always people who are on drugs who talk to themselves or attack people. There are many defenseless mentally ill people. Who do you think the bag ladies are? Crazy women running around with no social service to protect them. There are many more now because of President Reagan's federal court system. New York is an open-air mental hospital.

The best thing to do in order to live peacefully is to get away from the center of it all. But you can't always do that. Carmencita was getting worse and worse and died of depression within a few weeks of having checked into King's County Hospital. Her godmother made an appearance at the hospital with several friends to cause a scene. They were crying and insulting Miguelito. They threw all the African powers and major curses at him. But he was tough as nails. The godmother messed with him. She wanted to get him out of Red Hook. She stood in front of the door to the house and blew Saint Raphael dust to scare him away. Since he didn't believe in anything, he dealt with it. One day, the witch sent a gang of bums after him.

"I'll get even with you," she told him in a soft voice when she saw him in the bodeguita.

The bums got him in a Brooklyn Bridge bar and gave him a good beating. Miguelito never got into brawls. He was never nasty, none of that, but the old lady wanted to have her way with him. Since the police almost never went by those places, no one picked him up. And he couldn't run like before. After so much back and forth with that damn old lady, he finally moved to Chelsea.

"She threw me to the dogs, Julián."

"They're small dogs. If you want, stay here with us. Where three eat, four eat."

I put a couch in the living room for him and started to look for a room for him in Chelsea. Plácido helped me. We went to almost all the buildings in the neighborhood. We went up and down 19th Street. Nothing was worth it. The available rooms didn't have a bathroom inside of them. They were hovels with very bad heat.

That was when it occurred to me, "Look, Miguelito, we're going to Bartolo's banana field. They know me there, and they're going to find you something."

Bartolo's banana field, although it sounds funny, was a building full of Cubans on 8th Avenue between 22nd and 23rd. The rooms weren't big, but they did have their own bathroom and kitchenette. We spoke with the super. He was from Baracoa and also married to a Nuyorican. He was a good friend of mine.

We waited a couple of days to get him into a room on the 5th floor. The owner had died and the police had to give permission for it to be occupied again. The old man didn't have any heirs. He was a Cuban musician from a group called Yumurí. He came here in the 20s and was a tough guy from Baracutey. When the police saw so much junk, they made them throw everything in the garbage. But Miguelito kept the furniture and the boxes filled with clothing. He painted the room and moved in.

A lot of Latino bars and restaurants were opening on 8th Avenue. But Miguelito still did what he was used to: going to El Barrio to bet on the cocks. Cocks were and still are an illegal game in this country because of the fights and the animal rights organizations. But that didn't matter. Latinos still arranged hidden cockfights in basements in El Barrio and Brooklyn. I'd go a lot. I still go sometimes. Cocks are very lively, although the fight is very bloody. I've seen close friends get hurt and scarred over a heated fight in an galley. No one likes to lose. If the animal gets hurt, they act as if someone laid a hand on their wife in public. We Hispanics don't have cold blood like the North Americans. We don't know how to lose. Sportsmanship belongs to them. Wouldn't you agree?

Carmencita's death left Miguelito paralyzed. But time heals everything. Time is like a huge aspirin. Once he moved, he continued part-time at the restaurants in the area. In his free time, he'd set up a table at the 23rd Street flea market. He usually did this on Saturday and Sunday mornings. We divided the rest of the time at the table. Celia went with our daughter in the afternoon and sold what came in from the nearby towns. Professional junk sellers travel a lot. The bulk of the business comes from outside the city. They go to houses and gather old stuff. Then sell it at wholesale prices. We specialized in lamps with plastic shades and costume jewelry. Since I never had a car, I couldn't go anywhere to buy anything. I've always had good contacts though because of Miguelito. He can move mountains. Although he's a little crazy, he does know how to sell. But he didn't save. I did my best, but he messed everything up. That's when Celia called me to task one day, "Listen, Miguelito is your friend, not your kid."

"Look, Honey, don't get involved. Everything's taken care of here at home, right?"

"But you're losing out. He doesn't live up to his part of the deal."

Miguelito was going through a very rough time. We experienced many setbacks together. Later on, my wife was more understanding because she was a saint. She still is. I give her credit for it. In Miguelito's case, it's very sad to feel like an artist and unable to do anything about it. Even I can understand that without being a priest or psychologist.

I knew little about my family. Yara would write once in a while. She was the only one. According to her, my brother Pascual worked like a mule to support his kids. My mother was obviously older and still stuck doing the same things. Hopeless in the same old house. I'd send her some money because I couldn't really do anything else. My sister thanked me for it in her letters.

I sent her photos of my daughter in Central Park. My sister went crazy over them. She was the only thing that I was proud of despite everything. Since Yara was born here, I'm the only one she speaks Spanish with. She doesn't understand much about Cuba. That's what really bothers me most. I can't do anything about it. I feel like my feet and hands are tied behind my back. Sometimes I see case stories, as they're called here, on TV and I laugh. No one has told my story or even anything like it. They show marriage conflicts, adolescent sex cases, or a woman who can't have children.

But the life of a man who is a world away from his daughter? Never.

I sent her to public school and made her speak Spanish at home. However, when she stepped out of the house everything was in English.

"My child, you have to speak Spanish well."

"Okay, Pa. And why don't you speak English well?" she'd answer me.

That's my daughter. She's quite a smart ass. And very stubborn. I can't blame her for her apathy because fear made her act like that. She doesn't want to know anything about politics; she doesn't want to understand it.

"I'm very busy, Pa," she'd say in English.

Luckily, my wife is different. She was the first to get me interested in the protests in Washington during the Vietnam War. She didn't even wait for Miguelito. "Let's go, Julián. Many people are dying on both sides for no reason. Let's go!"

We went down there in caravans. We'd usually leave from La Casa de las Américas. Back then La Casa was on Broadway and not on 14th Street like it is today. I was never colder in my life. I don't know if it's because Washington has that big river, the Potomac, and there are gusts of wind, or because we spent hours outside with only a Cuban sandwich or lentil soup in our stomachs. My daughter was studying during those years at a college in New York and people protested—professors, students, employees—and she followed. But just for the thrill of it. Her friends came to pick her up at home to take her to the meetings in Union Square.

That's where she met her boyfriend, a 6'6" American. A decent guy, but a little silly. He distanced her from us because they fell in love. Wherever she'd go, he'd follow. For a big blond guy with skin as white as milk, an olive-skinned girl with black eyes like my sister's was like hitting the lottery. At sixteen, my daughter behaved like a woman. He almost never talked to me. He's a shy boy, doesn't say much, you can count on him around the house, but he is not ambitious. He's had the same job since they got married; he's a bouncer, as they're called here, in a sport-clothing store in New Jersey, where they've lived for nine years now. My daughter has him wrapped around her little finger. I say to him in Spanish, "Ron, can you believe that Yara is in the musical group Las Jardineras." Of course, he doesn't understand a thing, but he laughs. He doesn't miss a step. Wherever she goes, he follows.

"Ronald, politics help change things."

"No, Tony. Money does."

He calls me Tony because he doesn't want to say Julián. I respect him but I spend all my time arguing with him. The same thing happens with Celia. That's why we aren't close. They also live in another state, in another atmosphere, in a bubble. I don't know. It's like a curtain has been put up between the two of us. But she's the light of my life. I love her more than anyone else in my life.

When they go to Seattle for Christmas to see Ronald's parents, they leave the grandchildren here with us. That's when I feel happy. My older grandson Alan is totally Cuban. He's nothing like his father. The girl is blond, but she has tan skin. She's going to be very beautiful. They named her Alice after Ron's mother, who we only know from pictures because she never came to New York. I keep my grandson close to me. He knows as much about Cuba as any other real Latino. He draws maps of the Island and the Malecón and El Morro lighthouse. He's proud of his heritage: both the Cuban and the Puerto Rican sides. The girl is younger, but I'm taking her for the same ride. Celia and I have taught them the few words in Spanish that they know. Because it's so difficult to find a cassette of the Cuban National Anthem, I haven't been able to teach it to them yet. But now I'm trying to get one from the club where they have it on tape. I wouldn't want them to not know about their roots. I want them to know the truth. My blood's important to me. It seems to me that I've never left Cuba.

The streets of New York aren't like the streets in other places. A street in this city can be very happy in one stretch and very sad in another. Or they're very opulent like Park Avenue in the area of

Midtown and then get poor towards Uptown, all along El Barrio. If you see Park Avenue around the *marketa*, you can't imagine what it's like around Grand Central Station. Wall Street, where the stock market is, is like a beehive. There you run into the real mainstream of this country. Wall Street is Uncle Sam's wallet.

The streets have also seen their days and some even resemble great avenues because of their width, popularity, and businesses. Others are famous for their extravagance or pornography like Christopher Street and 42nd. Broadway is the longest street in New York and known for its cinemas and theaters. 47th is a gold mine. That's where all the celebrity jewelers are, mostly Jewish. But 23rd is the one I know best, the street of my time, the one with the cheapest businesses in Chelsea. It's wide like an avenue and also freezing cold in February because it gets the winds from 6th, 7th, and 8th Avenues. The winds come from the Hudson with gusts that throw you on the ground. The Chelsea Hotel, where many famous writers and artists have lived, is right there. It's not the same anymore; now it's a seedy drug joint. Although some decent people still live there, retired artists or second-class writers who are full of themselves say, "I live in the Chelsea Hotel." Reputations are hard to change.

23rd was once the busiest street in Chelsea. The buildings with stone facades and iron balconies, like the hotel, are still in tact. The old Irish descendents of the neighborhood's original habitants call the corner of 23rd and 6th the Times Square of New York of the turn of the century because a lot of activity went on there. You still see old Irishmen taking out their little dogs for a walk, in the cafés on 8th, and smoking their pipes. The sweet odor of the tobacco gives them away. Irishmen are chimneys.

Many Cubans work on 23rd. The Ortuño brothers had a factory on 23rd between 6th and 7th where they made metal shelves for offices. Many of those Cubans were my friends. We'd get together in a café called the Stewart on 6th and 23rd. It was a very busy café, especially after six in the evening. We talked about everything there. It was entertaining. The Stewart was very Latino. That's why very few women went. We were in our element there. I'm sorry to say that it's no longer there.

I used to go out a lot more. Things are different now. The street is full of *joloperos*, as they call certain Italians and Latinos, and you run the risk of being mugged on any corner. A *jolope* is an assault with a hand weapon. It comes from the English word "holdup," but it's a pretty common word to say in Spanish. People always use it here. Bognano was one of the most famous *joloperos* in Manhattan. They've already arrested him. He was an Italian with a thick bush of hair on his chest. He left behind an entire family of *joloperos*. They have New York scared to death. They multiply by the dozen. They jump from neighborhood to neighborhood. They particularly like train stations, stairs, and the subway.

19th Street is something else. I've been on this street for more than thirty years. I know it like the back of my hand. It's a quiet street, although they've opened some Criolla food joints that sell pot. It's a front for the sale of marijuana. The one underneath my house is famous for selling all types of stuff, although I wouldn't know for sure. They're Ecuadorians and they stay away from me. To tell you the truth, I haven't seen anything suspicious yet. But I wouldn't set foot in there to even have a coffee just in case. The police can arrive one day and arrest everyone. I try to avoid those tangles. Other than that, 19th Street is calm with many warehouses, some design stores, and real estate agencies.

Nowadays, Union Square is the real meeting point for workers in New York. It's relatively close to my house. In winter it's just like any old park with benches covered in ice. Even when it's like that, the joint sellers take it over like they did to Washington Square. Cars drive around the square and customers sometimes don't even have to get out of their cars. Union Square is a historical place, full of hawkers selling whatever they can. They're beggars who sell newspapers, hardware, and candy. Some even write a song and try to sell it. There, you'll also find the Salvation Army, Jewish refugees, and workers on strike . . . That's what Union Square looks like on Saturdays and Sundays. But the place has also been known for being the center of leftist and radical group movements for some time now. The May 1st events in New York start there. Any political parade starts at the northern part of Union Square. It seems that they purposely gave it that name because it fits like a glove. Besides being the intersection of streets like Broadway, 14th Street, 4th Avenue and others, it unites people of all political parties, religions, and races.

Sometimes you find a surprise on the streets of New York. I've seen them change overnight. Buildings such as the Metropolitan Opera House have been demolished to put up nothing special. The rich don't respect historical monuments. They tear down an old building and put up a bunch of green glass and metal. That's what happened with many New York hotels and theaters. Money is an excuse for everything.

The feel of a neighborhood and the flavor of a street can disappear in a flash. All you need is someone to think about buying a plot of land or starting a business. Skyscrapers don't do anything for the sense of community. Thank God the Public Library, City Hall, the Post Office, and Cooper Union, where Martí spoke, are still standing. All those buildings really impressed me when I first got here. You think they're so big, like in 3-D, and you don't want to go in. We've gone to the Metropolitan Museum of Art and the Museum of Natural History with my daughter. However, even after having been here for so many years, I've never gone up to the top of the Empire State Building. My wife is scared of elevators, but I'm not. I haven't gone up because I don't even like to go on planes. Height is ugly. The Empire State is much bigger than the Eiffel Tower. It measures 1,250 feet high. For years it was the tallest building in the world. But now they put up the World Trade Center, two very tall towers at the most southern tip of the city, and the Empire State Building looks like a miniature.

Money is an excuse for everything. Here, they don't respect historical monuments because they don't respect historical figures. Now they use the name George Washington for a brand of refrigerators. They put a wig and morning coat on a handy-man in front of the camera, and this guy introduces himself as George Washington and tries to sell the thing. He opens the door, shows the little drawers, the ice cube trays . . . It's the highlight of Channel 47!

Before, it was better to walk in the city: it was safer. There was not as much perversion, not as much crime; people wore blue and gray. Today there's no respect for elegance. Clothing defines the neighborhoods of New York. Now you can go to Lincoln Center wearing sneakers and a jacket. My daughter is really into that. I'm conservative. However, youth does rule. On St. Mark's, a punk area of the East Village, the young girls go to the Ukrainian orthodox churches with their hair dyed green and their lips painted black. The boys shave their heads, leave a mohawk or a braid in the back and tie a colorful ribbon around it. They don't believe in anything. Some are worse than a possum with a big head. We're living in a very strange time. Luckily young people are still opposed to nuclear war. Thank God, because despite everything, life is very beautiful. You go through hard times, make the same mistakes two or three times, regret a thousand things, but always have the desire to live.

That's why I don't understand many immigrants. I've met them here, in restaurants, factories, markets, and dance halls. They sacrificed years and years to buy a little plot of land in Puerto Rico, Colombia, or Ecuador; or to send money to their children, but they don't see them. Years go by without seeing them. They don't see them grow up during the important years like five to ten. I know many situations like that. In my opinion, they're twisted, mistaken people. How can someone have a five-year-old child in Cochabamba and not go see him or her because they've spent their money on the Bergen Line buying a $5,000 bedroom set for their house? They're committed to paying it off for years. And during that time, their children are growing up in another country, with other people. They're no longer their children. It's true that in many places there isn't work, but I don't know what's worse: to lose a child or a job.

I wouldn't live far away from my daughter. She has grown up here, as I said earlier. She speaks English better than Spanish. She's American despite me shoving Cuban things in her face. But when she fights with her husband, she's 100% Cuban. It comes right out of her. I couldn't live without my daughter. That's why I don't understand people who measure happiness with material things. There's no doubt that many Cubans have made money here. Cubans are full of initiatives and very hardworking people. But money isn't all there is to life. What do they do with the money if they have to deal with the terrible cold of winter? If they're far from their families? If they don't have a way into society's mainstream? They buy a Cadillac and prance around the streets. Or they rent luxury suits and throw sweet-sixteen parties with custom-made dresses. They get their pictures taken in studios on the Bergen Line, send the photos to Cuba, and then it happens all over again, and they still don't have anyone to help them out.

I'm not criticizing North Americans, it's just their style. They're individualists, but Cubans are straightforward, they look for companionship. That's why life in the United States is very solitary for me despite being married and having my daughter and two or three friends. If you want to play dominos you go to La Casa de las Américas on Sundays. There isn't anything else to do. But everything is tense; people's nerves are always on end. They're always thinking about work and how far apart everything is. Very few people still take the train after seven at night, especially the older people. Who wants to be the victim of a holdup? Who wants their head spilt in half? Women have been assaulted on the train or raped trying to open the door of their house. It's dangerous. Every day the mayor announces that they're going to wipe out the murderers and drug addicts. Sometimes they sweep the Lower East Side, but they don't touch Chelsea, Midtown, and 42nd Street. The police are scared of those people. I don't know how they're going to fix the problem.

New York is very busy. It's possibly the center of the world, I don't doubt it, but it's a very dangerous city to live in. I was chosen out of a hat. There's nothing I can do about it. Luck is granted only once. And at my age no one risks making the wrong decision. In Cuba, I know I'd live more peacefully. I'd be happier. But I can't be selfish, because after all, my wife, my daughter, and my grandchildren were born here. They belong here more than I do.

"Pa, you're crazy," Yara María says to me in English when she sees me reading the newspaper from there or telling my grandchildren about Havana or the Sierra Maestra. I'm up-to-date with the latest news from Cuba. Nothing gets by me. I'm following the trail of the Revolution. My sister writes me, and because the letters take one month to get here, I answer her early, because I already know what she's going to tell me. It's as if I lived there.

I was one of the first to find out about what happened at Moncada. Since I'd already heard about Fidel, I said to everyone here, "It wasn't Carlos Prío Socarrás or Millo Ochoa. Those guys don't have balls. Fidel and his men were the ones who did it."

On July 30th, his name appeared in *La Prensa* for the first time as "Leader Killed in the Mountains." I was right. From that day on we all talked about Fidel. When he came to Palm Garden to speak, he was already considered a leader in the Cuban community here. Palm Garden was a dance hall on 51st and 8th Avenue. I don't know if it's still there, but it's an historic site for us. Fidel Castro and Juan Manuel Márquez spoke there. That's where the two of them dotted their "i"s. They clearly stated the Revolution's program. Juan Manuel lost his suitcase and we had a collection in his honor and gave him new clothing. He was extremely happy. He even got all emotional. From New York they went to Mexico and from there to the Sierra Maestra. In 1957, the North American journalist Herbert Mathews was the one who announced in the newspapers here that the guerrilla was in the Sierra. The poor people, the factory and restaurant workers, immediately supported the 26th of July Movement. That was when they started collections to gather money and buy weapons and supplies for the guerrillas.

In New York the history of the 26th of July Movement goes way back. I say in New York because it was here where it gained strength, but the birthplace was really in Bridgeport, Connecticut, where there was a very dense Cuban colony. That history must be documented: the houses where we gathered, the places where Fidel was, where Camilo Cienfuegos lived . . . all those places are there, but no one has done anything to acknowledge them. It's the same thing with the house where José Martí lived on Front Street and on 29th. It's as if nothing happened there, no mention of Martí. Martí spoke at Cooper Union during the memorial to Karl Marx. The tablet on the wall there on St. Mark's Street lists many speakers—Abraham Lincoln is one of them—but it doesn't say anything about Martí. And he lived in this city so many years. There's a statue of Martí on Central Park South, at 59th and 6th, and for years now a group of us go there with a floral offering. But it's a risk to go there. The counter-revolutionary organizations crowd the place in the morning, wanting to claim Martí for themselves. Sometimes big uproars, with punches, clubs, and personal insults break out. That's the way it is and all of us go every January 28th at four in the afternoon rain or shine.

Here, any type of revolutionary work is very risky. We aren't really a clandestine group, but it's as if we were one. The 26th of July Movement made Cuban emigrants more politically aware. It was a mess; no one knew where to step. There were more political organizations and clubs for exiles than there were for revolutionaries. And many had both. I was never director or anything like that. To tell the truth, Miguelito was the one who got me excited about the 26th of July. He was suspicious of all the Cubans here. He was right. The best gathered on the 26th of July, at least the newest and the bravest, real people, without unreasonable expectations. There were a lot of organizations here: Ateneo Cubano, Club Interamericano del Bronx, Liceo Cubano, Casa Cubana, Club José Martí, etc. Some had to be careful because Batista's consulate put plenty of pressure on them.

In my opinion, the 26th of July Movement was born of the very best, mostly young people with a sense of civility. But it wasn't only because of those clubs that things happened. One of the principal organizers of the 26th of July Movement here was José Llanusa. He said, "We're done relaxing. In New York there's only one organization, and it's the 26th." That's the way it was. Everyone agreed with Fidel. The problem was that some of the clubs were riddled with racists or people who were well-off. So it was a question of bringing the masses together.

In those years, there were hardly any communists, only in the Club José Martí. Everyone else supported other political parties and ideas. Everyone was very restless. Fidel was the one who put things in order. He always spoke clearly. If they didn't understand him it's because they were used to hearing people talk about nonsense, about fraud and things that weren't in the homeland's best interest. That's all. He said, "If I go, I arrive; if I arrive, I go in; if I go in, I win." That's how he was. When he got off the boat *Granma*, on the coast of Las Coloradas, we poor people in New York already had his back.

La Prensa described the combat in Alegría de Pío as a fatal hit to the rebels. I remember a communist Jew of Russian descent saying in the Casa Cuba one night, "They're guerrillas. They're hidden underneath the roots of the trees. They're going to come out. Just you wait." He was very supportive of the 26th of July Movement.

That Jewish man was named Baker. He was always talking about how he was a baker; of course that's where Baker comes from. He gave a lot of money for the Sierra Maestra cause. There were other foreigners like him, but we always remember Baker. When Israel thanked Egypt for the Suez Canal, Baker was embarrassed. He was like a fireproof man. In 1960 Abraham G. Baker was the head of the Club Amigos de la Revolución Cubana in the United States.

The 26th of July Movement brought together very good people. For the first time real humble people, factory workers, electricians, waiters and people with their own minds, united for a single cause.

Batista never imagined that. Surely he thought that the consulate could control it all with their dogs. His plan backfired on him.

Many refined people got scared when they saw things turn around. Especially when they saw the blacks come down from the Sierra Maestra as commanders and captains. They got scared and changed their hats. The Ateneo Cubano gave some money, but when they heard Fidel's speeches and saw Juan Almeida on the front page of the newspaper as a war hero, they cracked because many were racists and bourgeois. But the group of the 26th had the best of the emigrants.

I only helped out at the Club like Miguelito did. That was all the time we had. Between the restaurant and the flea market we couldn't think about anything else. We simply couldn't cope. Every day we got information straight from the Sierra Maestra. Each branch—because the 26th had around forty branches between New York and Jersey City—gave a report of the guerillas' movements almost daily. A lot of propaganda was distributed, along with medicine, bullets . . .

I remember very clearly that once a petition arrived directly from the Sierra: Bullets for Bazookas. What a mess it was here! Everyone was determined to raise money and get bullets. It wasn't easy because there was tight control of American bazooka bullets. Even with those conditions, we found about a thousand and they were sent to the Sierra through secret channels. That was a big accomplishment for us because we achieved the impossible. Other weapons were taken to the Mambí, a restaurant on 161st and St. Nicolas on the west side. How did they get out of here? Who knows? Today the counterrevolutionaries want to imitate the 26th of July Movement, but they don't even have a strategy, nor are they honest. That's why they fail. Only an ideology like that one can do what was done. I have my carnet from the 26th of July with all the stamps I bought each week. Fidel signed some of those carnets. Almost all are in the Museum of the Revolution in Havana—one of the places where I want to go some day because a part of our lives is there. My wife's life too.

to work. She had a dollar sign tattooed on her forehead. She came here without hardly any contacts, with the idea of opening a café. At least, that was her plan.

She went to live with some of her compatriots on 29th Street, but she never brought us there. It was all a big mystery. She told us that her compatriots owned a little falafel restaurant in the Village. They gave her a basement with a bathroom to live in. Eva didn't understand the Revolution. She didn't even talk about it. She was apolitical. She wanted to make money here. But the cigarettes destroyed her lungs. During the first January snowstorm, Celia had to take her to St. Vincent's Hospital where she was declared terminally ill. She coughed and had a shrill ringing in her ear that lasted about ten seconds. You got the chills just listening to her because she didn't do anything else but talk about her plans for the future. The Lebanese community gave her nothing but misery for her sickness. Eva got a daily saline solution treatment and a weekly blood transfusion. Miguelito and I took care of her as much as we could. Everything we had went towards hospital bills, especially to pay for the medicine. Eva had just arrived and she didn't have anything set up. It was a disaster. On top of that, the Lebanese people didn't want to have anything to do with her. They rented out the basement to someone else. There was nothing left for me to do but take Eva to die in my house. My daughter still remembers her smoking and coughing. She says to me once in a while, "Pa, that was really a nightmare."

The strangest things in the world happen here. Miguelito had a friend who was a Lutheran pastor. He gave Eva a funeral. The Lebanese didn't dare show their faces. We buried her on 9th Street on the Lower East Side. It was the right thing to do. Even my daughter sent some white lilies. We still get letters at home from her friends in Cuba. We have them all there, sealed of course. We don't even know who they're from or who to give them to. Even though she had a lot of friends in Cuba, Eva was a very strange woman.

I spent the rest of my life on 23rd Street. That's the way it's been and that's all there is to tell. That's the thing about Chelsea. It traps you in and there's no way of getting out. It's like a vice. Months go by and I don't go above 34th Street. I've also become quite sedentary in this country. I've calmed down because if you don't limit yourself to one neighborhood, the octopus entangles you. Here you can't walk carelessly from one place to another. Nor can you go to some place without rhyme or reason and just hang out there because you feel like it. No, here you have to stick to what's yours so that you aren't left alone. I've been going to the same café for years. That's where I see people. The waiter is a Boricua, although that doesn't really mean anything. He knows what Cubans like to eat, he reads the Cuban newspapers, and his daughter is married to a man from Pinar del Río. That's the way it is here, everything's mixed. That's why the bastards call this neighborhood La Korea.

In summer everyone gets outdoors. People fill the streets. For example, Puerto Ricans like to be out in the sun, playing dominos, and standing on the corner. Cubans aren't much different. On the other hand, winter forces you to stay home. That's why television has been so successful in this country. You get up, you put on the Weather Channel. If they say it's going to be very cold you crank up the heat and watch TV. It's torture if you don't have a remote control to change the channel. Television is a mode of propaganda. At least with the remote control you can press mute and avoid the commercials. It's not that bad if it's a musical program, but if it's a movie or an interview, it's the worst. I know people who get home and right away turn the thing on. They don't even watch it or listen to it, but they have it on until four or five in the morning. They're usually single. In my opinion, they like to always hear the murmur of it for company. There are those who put on the TV to fall asleep. That's if they don't have a cat. Almost everybody has a cat, especially the North Americans. Hispanics are busy with their children or close relatives and a cat becomes a nuisance.

Ms. Goodman, the Jewish woman in charge of the flea market on 23rd, has six cats. First she feeds the cats and then herself. Each cat has its own name: Troy, Waterloo, Trafalgar, Dien Bien Puh, Ayacucho and Calabaza. They have those names because Ms. Goodman is a progressive woman and has studied wars. Calabaza, which means a type of pumpkin in Spanish, is the youngest. She liked the name because she heard us say it a couple of times. When we showed her a *calabaza* from the *marketa*, the first thing she said was, "It's just like my new cat."

Our *calabaza* is a more intense yellow than the ones they have here in the States. Ms. Goodman's cat is a very pretty *calabaza* yellow, but he changes his coat every week. You can't get close to him or else you get covered with his hair.

Frieda Goodman started the flea market on 23rd. She got the idea for the market because of her contacts with the Democratic Party. It really came in handy for us. Miguelito made much more than I did, but even so, no one made a decent salary. Tips were the crux of the restaurant business. We both benefited from Frieda's little market. She didn't really need to do it, but like many Americans, she liked to do something humanitarian, something altruistic.

The flea market was like a type of club in a small, narrow space. It was financed with the rent that the vendors paid for the tables. They had political meetings at the locale and organized trips to Washington and to the UN to protest the Vietnam War and racial discrimination. Miguelito got involved with the program. Soon after, the Jewish woman made him a janitor and allowed him to sleep in a little room in the back by the bathroom. The atmosphere intensified because of the type of place it was and because of Miguelito's friends.

The Jewish lady became so happy. To sum it up, she owned a restaurant on Columbus between 71st and 72nd and the club was an extra. Ms. Goodman wanted to collect funds for the Party and do charity work. She did it by renting out tables. She got up to six or seven dealers in the flea market. But we, I mean, Miguelito, Celia, and I, were always there. She was bossy and overbearing, and wanted to control everything. That's why people would leave after a few days. They couldn't stand her. The type of old, selfish, greedy flea-market vendor couldn't stand her.

We weren't that way. Miguelito organized many benefits there for Latin American artists who came to New York and didn't really know that much about the place. With a certain percent of the donations, we got some money together. We converted the space into a meeting place for Latinos. We had fairs. We sold lots of costume jewelry, political campaign posters, coins, stamps, and books. The Jewish woman was fine with it provided that we paid her for the use of the locale for her political agenda. That's how we took advantage of the situation in order to make some money. She showed up less and less each time. She trusted Miguelito and told him, "You are my Saint Peter. Here, have the keys to the place." He felt like the owner and the boss of the place. Right away he set up shop. We sold a lot, I'm not going to deny it, because old costume jewelry is always in style. But more money was spent on benefit parties and exhibits by Hispanic artists.

Chelsea was livelier in the 60s. People became fans of the club and when Miguelito would run out of ideas, people would ask him for performances by so-and-so. They were known names, people from El Barrio or Brooklyn, with their drums and guitars. Any old excuse would be good enough to get a group to play bombas and guarachas. He went from an artist to the neighborhood businessman. The Jewish woman checked up on him every once in a while, and she had reason to do so. The market became a café with clients who were just there to waste time: gays, bohemians.

Ms. Goodman wasn't religious but she did water fasts for several days to cleanse her body. She participated in hunger strikes to support the Native Americans. Her abdomen shrunk and her stomach became a raisin. She was proud of her actions. She was a liberal democrat, that's all. She didn't sleep. She took pills to get rid of her appetite and stay awake. When she'd go to the market, she'd sit by the door and watch the customers. If she noticed something strange about any of them, any sign of defiance, she'd call them over and give them a really long sermon about morals and what it means to be a citizen.

Miguelito won her over because he went along with her. At times she'd go to the protests with us, but she was a burden. She'd always try to get all the attention. She needed to be the center of things. When she didn't have a headache, she had a cold or some other kind of pain. She was a disaster! At the protests, in the rain and the cold, there was nothing that woman wouldn't do to attract attention. Each one of us carried a thermos of water for Ms. Goodman's cravings. When it was time to eat something, she'd get very mean. She hardly ever took a bite of a sandwich. Everything tasted like plastic to her. Everything had chemical preservatives. Everything was artificial. On the way back, we practically had to carry her over our shoulders. Ah, Frieda Goodman, we'll never forget you!

Between Celia and Miguelito, we kept the flea market going. The people in Chelsea got used to going. And although they didn't go to buy anything, they always walked away with something. It was a great way to sell Latino-style costume jewelry, diamonds, rhinestones, aquamarine earrings and rings of all sizes. Silver and gold! José Díaz hooked us up with a connection in Chinatown where we'd buy things for very cheap at wholesale prices. It was generally Celia who'd go do the buying because Miguelito took advantage of his free hours to do part-time gigs as a soloist in some Spanish cafés in Midtown. The Episcopal Church sponsored us so we didn't have to pay taxes. Here, that's a real drag; taxes eat people alive. There are three kinds: municipal, state, and federal, or income tax. Since I'm married, I pay a little less. But since Miguelito is single, he has to pay higher taxes. Well, being the stray bullet that he is, no one has wanted to marry him. They run away from him like the devil on the cross.

People will do just about anything to avoid paying taxes. There are those who put themselves down as a reverend of a chapel, like the ex-president Jimmy Carter. And those who marry a North

American for money. And those who even change their nationality and address. Basically, as I said before, it's a real drag.

After a lot of back and forth we finally got Ms. Goodman to allow us to sell coffee and cigarettes. We don't need to pay anyone for maintenance and cleaning because Miguelito is in charge of that. Ms. Goodman gives free consultations on Mondays from eleven in the morning to three in the afternoon. She gets poor people from El Barrio and they ask her about their problems and needs. Sometimes they want a mattress or a refrigerator, or money to return to Puerto Rico or Santo Domingo. But most of them are looking for work. Ms. Goodman's mission is altruist; she does charity work. In the end, she doesn't fix much, but she believes that she's doing a very good deed. She asks whoever wants to be a member for letters of recommendation, and another letter from the place where they work. Being a member doesn't yield any great benefit. It's only to support Ms. Goodman's cause, her flea market, her consultations, and the rent. Members get a discount if they buy something and can go to the events without giving a donation. That's it.

We sell *The Daily World* and give out leftist pamphlets. We haven't been able to put up any Cuban propaganda because Ms. Goodman doesn't want it. She's very old now. She's scared of Cuban terrorists. And although they've never gone there, some years ago they set off a bomb in La Casa de las Américas that destroyed the entrance.

More than 300,000 people are unemployed in New York. We formed the Comité de Acción de Desempleados, or a group to help the city's unemployment problem. Basically, we try to stop people from getting evicted or having their electricity and telephone service cut off. We also try to end unemployment, and provide food stamps and medical assistance. It's nothing compared to all the problems there are, but we try to chip away at the bigger issue. At least, we're doing something.

I didn't come from a very politically active family, but I do come from a very poor background and that's something you don't forget. I can't overlook injustices. That's why my liver has been poisoned here. I've become pretty politically active seeing what goes on. When they were still selling *Bohemia* in New York, I'd pay $5 for a copy. I wanted to read about the Agrarian Reform, the Revolutionary government's education plans and, of course, Fidel's speeches. Then they stopped selling it. Once in a while we could get it at La Casa de las Américas to be more or less up to date with what was going on in Cuba. That's our only incentive in this country.

Hispanic television is very bad. My wife watches it every day for the soap operas. I don't. I just watch the news, baseball games, and boxing matches. But she watches everything, even the cooking programs in English. And she exercises to stay in shape. When my daughter lived at home, Celia couldn't watch the Hispanic channels and there was no way for me to see the baseball games or boxing matches. Yara María would spend hours watching musicals and American movies. They were so difficult to understand. Even though I've been here for many years, I still can't understand movies in English. I don't know if it's because of the speakers or how fast they talk. I sometimes leave the theater just like I went in. It's different when I go with Celia because we sit in the way back and she translates the hard to understand dialogues in my ear. If it weren't for her, I'd think it were Chinese. English is like that.

Around 1966 Miguelito met Mercedes Matamoros at the flea market. She had just become the widow of a Cuban musician. She had lived at 81st and Amsterdam since 1945. She was married when she came here. She liked it, so she stayed. Mercedes and my wife became very good friends. She had a connection or way into the music business because her husband left her two songs he composed before shooting himself. Since some Latino groups still play them, she gets some money because she holds the copyright. Mercedes has been able to get by in this city because of that and from selling English courses to Hispanics.

They met at the Democratic Club. She came to ask Ms. Goodman for advice and Miguelito followed her all the way to Lexington Avenue, or so he says. Mercedes was born in a *solar* in a very poor neighborhood in Marianao back in Cuba. During Grau's government, she married the man who brought her to New York. They came on the steamboat *Cuba* with a contract to play at the Chateau Madrid. Later, as is often the case, the group fell apart and Mercedes's husband was out on the street. He didn't have enough money to return to Havana and on top of that he got a malignant growth on his neck. He shot himself in the basement of a Latino building on the Upper West Side. Mercedes was left with nothing, but she was lucky enough to find work in a factory, and after some time, get together with Miguelito. The two of them came from poverty; they understood each other well. She helped him to get himself together and in return he made her happy to be alive.

Mercedes always comes up with something to do. When she can't sell English courses, she sews for people or does some housekeeping. I've seen Mercedes sell an English course by giving a Dominican man the run around. She called the man over and asked him if he already spoke English well. The man said "yes." So she said to him in Spanish, "Let's see. How do you say the word *casa* in English?"

And when the man told her "home" without softening the "o" she caught him in the act and showed him where he'd gone wrong. The Dominican was impressed and Mercedes sold him the course with a false discount that she invented on the spot. She supported her mother and two sisters in Cuba with those tricks until the triumph of the Revolution. That's why it's incredible to her that her sisters don't need money for medicine today. Mercedes goes to Cuba when she has some extra money. She tried to get Miguelito and me to go back and visit. She never liked this country, but she had to do what she could in order to support her family. She spent her entire youth here and has her retirement pension from the union. It's too late for her to go back and start over again. She and Miguelito make a good couple. Even though she said he could stay at her apartment, he won't leave the little storage room at the flea market for anything in the world.

Ms. Goodman doesn't get along very well with her. But her days are numbered. She turned eighty a couple of days ago. She's about to leave the club. Mercedes doesn't go over there very much so she doesn't see the Jewish woman. Miguelito has practically hogged control of the merchandise and tables. The only thing left for Ms. Goodman to do there is give her weekly sermons about democracy and altruism.

That's the flea market and that's my life in Chelsea. I left Cuba to escape hunger and I arrived here at a time when you could still find work. But I fell in the trap. I've had fun, I can't say I didn't, but I haven't been happy. You can't be happy in a foreign land. You can't deny where you come from. Cuban roots are very strong.

I still haven't told you about the time when El Liborio went bankrupt and I was out of a job. Before Plácido died he recommended me to the landlord and they made me superintendent of the building where I live. We often call it *super* in Spanish here. In other words, I'm in charge of a six-story brownstone building with twenty-four apartments. I never forgot José Díaz's advice. I learned carpentry, electricity, and plumbing. Finally those skills have been useful to make a living serving others because that's the job of the super, a servant at the mercy of the renters. The only advantage is that you don't pay rent. The super is the only one in the building who has that deal. You live for free but with no freedom, no privacy, at the expense of the first crazy person who comes and knocks on your door to ask you for a hammer or complain about a leak.

My friends look me as a super and ask me if I've run out of gas because I've always been such a fighter. It's not that. I still work so I can eat and occasionally put something in the bank for my grandchildren. I stopped hoping to be something more, that's for sure. I'm never going to be somebody in this country. Or maybe I will if I hit the jackpot in the lotto. Then I'll really be something because I'm going to make a very big scandal in the newspapers. I'm going to send all my winnings to Cuba so that I can someday say, "I contributed a little grain of sand to the Revolution."

As I said, the super is a servant and a victim. I close my eyes and say to myself: "Damn it, Julián, why didn't you become an engineer, a lawyer, or a diplomat?"

The circle of life got me because the super is the one who pays for the broken plates. And this building is a dive. On the outside it's very pretty because it's one of the oldest brownstones in the neighborhood and the owner paints it almost every year. But inside it's a madhouse. When I moved here it wasn't like this. People had another way of living back then, another rhythm. There wasn't so much demoralization. But now there are more mentally sick on the street than in the hospitals. This building isn't that bad though compared to some others. The neighborhood supers know each other and we exchange stories. I've heard incredible things. If I told them, many people would call me a liar, or a storyteller. There are enough stories to write a book.

The super often serves as a psychiatrist. Especially in a building like this, where so many people live alone, without family, without close friends. Very strange people from all parts of the world. On Sundays we get together in my apartment with some friends: Mercedes, Miguelito, José Díaz, and Alfred McAdams, an Irishman obsessed with Latino music. I tell them what I have to deal with. They think it's a comedy show. They call me a liar, a fibber, and a thousand other things. And finally we start to laugh because as Celia says, "First tragedy, then comedy."

They know what I'm saying and they still don't believe me. In my opinion, it's very easy to swim out of water. If I hadn't gotten the job as super, I'd still be bumping and jolting around: from restaurant to workshop, to factory, or doing all kinds of tricks in order to survive. A man of my age in this country needs stability. New generations take over, especially in the factories. For a man over forty-five, his life becomes impossible if he doesn't have a job. The owners logically employ young people because they don't know anything about unions or workers' rights. So they get hired with a lower salary and work like dogs, twelve and fourteen hours a day to take their girlfriend to the movies or to buy drugs. That's what happens most of the time. It creates a fierce selfishness. Many become strikebreakers or they team up with the foreman. They're like patches to fix labor union problems and to replace the older generations. That's why I'll be a super until it's time to retire. I prefer to mess around with crazy people instead of shameless people and exploiters.

I get up early every day. I make breakfast for my wife and myself. I wake her up and we start to talk. She has always liked to sleep a lot. Also it's because she goes to sleep to the tune of Channel 41. She'll watch any movie in Spanish or English. It doesn't matter to her. But she always gets up as fresh as iceberg lettuce. We spend so much time talking. Lately I only talk about the building, it's my biggest headache.

Who would've known? My gosh. This place is a zoo! And I'm not exaggerating. Before accepting the position I thought a lot about it. But I gave in because some years ago I suffered from a kidney infection and since then I've only been able to work part-time jobs. So when Plácido died, I went down to 17th Street to pick up the certificate and take a course for supers. It was basically some instructions on how to deal with the boiler, or *boila* as we call it in Spanish. They also should've given me a course on how to be a shrink. But I guess it's too late, I already graduated.

The *boila* is the heart of the building. The super lives like a slave to it around the clock. They're either coal, oil, or gas. The one in my building is oil so I don't have to shovel coal, but it's still constant slave work. Since the super is really a servant, the tenants call you at any hour. They scream and stamp their feet like animals. "Super, I'm *freezando*," they say in Spanglish. And when I arrive, they either have a shutter open or haven't scotch-taped the doors. Some of those renters have serious problems in the head.

I'm not exaggerating. That's why I hide out in the basement.

The basement of this building isn't too big, but it's good enough for me to store the junk we sell and some old pieces of furniture. It's also how I get away from the world of the living. And they still go down there looking for me. One of the renters even found the master key and tried to open the door on me. I'm lucky I discovered her on time! Then she went to the landlord to tell him stories and gossip. The basement should technically be only for the building's materials and tools, but I use it for my stuff. After all, I've lived here for over thirty years.

I have it filled to the brim. The landlord Mr. Waterman is very intrigued, but I don't let him in. He has asked me if I have money hidden there because the only thing he thinks about is money. I tell him, "Look, Mr. Waterman, if you want, I'll take you down so you can see for yourself."

But he doesn't want to go with me because deep down he's a little scared of me. He's afraid I'll freak out on him. He's Jewish, sarcastic, and ambitious. Miguelito is the only one who's gone down to the basement with me when he comes to bring over stuff for the flea market or for the annual street fairs on 21st and 24th. The basement is my real home. It's where I can completely isolate myself. My wife yells at the tenants, "He's not here." I hear her and I laugh. That's how I get my revenge. That's how I strike back.

One afternoon Miguelito comes to the building with Durango Nieves. Durango was a human wreck and Miguelito became his benefactor. I already knew about Durango's state and what he was all about, but I hadn't seen him for years. In New York that happens a lot. Entire families live a few minutes away and they don't even see each other. Durango was running away from something, from someone, and I knew it but I didn't say anything. Miguelito wasn't going to play a dirty trick on me, however . . .

I let him sleep in the basement for a couple of days. I found him a mattress and a place where he could store his stuff. I gave him the key to the padlock. Everything was going well until one night. Durango had my instructions to frighten away any solicitors from the building and to warn the Pentecostals and the Gedeon

Evangelical Band not to bother the neighbors. In the building nobody wants to hear sermons of that kind. None of them are going to heaven anyway. Durango did his job, he took care of the junk down there for me and once in a while he came up to my apartment to have a coffee.

There was one thing that didn't sit well with me: Durango was Nuyorican like Celia and the two of them always spoke English to each other. I totally trusted her. My wife has always been there for me. But I didn't trust him. I only helped him out because of Miguelito. While he was living there he didn't make any effort to look for a job. He woke up at noon and didn't even clean the sleep out of his eyes. He blocked the entrance to the basement with a pile of old magazines. And the worst part is, he was disrespectful towards Celia. One night she lost it, she couldn't contain herself. She said to me, "Get him out of here soon." Upon seeing her with her eyes bulging out of her head, I asked her why, and to tell me the whole truth. At first she only told me half of it.

"Julián, I see him taking bags out of the basement when you're not here."

I sped down there and almost broke down the door on him. He reluctantly opened it for me and in order to enter, I had to push it because he pretended he was sleeping. I turned on the light and started to check out the junk. I couldn't find anything. I was blind.

"Who has told you these stories, Julián? If you want, I'll go sleep in the subway, but I've never been a thief."

He told me with such conviction! If my wife hadn't been the type to tell me everything, I would've let him stay there that night. Sometimes you can be a real idiot . . .

"Julián," Celia said to me, "get him out of here." She was very bothered.

"But tell me, what has that man done to you?"

"What has he done to me? Well he took out his parts in your kitchen, Julián. In front of me. He's an ungrateful pig."

Durango grabbed a piece of wood and threatened to kill me, but he was a coward. He froze when he saw my knife.

"That's a lie, Julián. Don't believe her."

The remedy was worse than the cure. He launched the piece of wood at my head, but he was unarmed. We fought and I stuck his right armpit. Upon seeing the blood, he ran out. He got lost from my house, from Chelsea, and I believe from New York.

Miguelito was avoiding me. He and Mercedes weren't guilty, but they did trust people too fast. That was the only unpleasant incident that happened in my basement. For the rest, as I already said, it's my refuge to escape from the world of the living. I've kept the largest collection of *Bohemia* in New York down there. I entertain myself by reading them when the zoo is calm, which is almost never. The fierce animals, when they're not whining to me about something, go from one side of the apartment to the other making noise for fun, as if they were looking for something.

I have a tenant over six feet tall who lives alone. He bought himself a sheepdog and when he gets home from the Heartley Restaurant, where he's a bartender, he starts to play with her. He whistles at her, throws her rubber balls, hits her . . . The dog is as big as he is. He takes her out to piss on the sidewalk until they're both tired. All of this goes on after three in the morning, and for no good reason. And he's one of the better ones. Around Christmas he gives me a good tip. He doesn't hide like the rest of the tenants. He throws out the garbage, and always says "good morning." When he drinks and starts to jump around with the dog inside the apartment, I want to kill him. Not so much because of the noise, but because of the avalanche of renters that knocks on my door or calls me on the phone to make him shut up. As if I had the right to do that! I already said it: he's the calmest in the building, even considering his bad habits. The rest of them are completely nuts.

I'm a full-time super. Once I tried to take care of public buildings as a security guard, but the night shifts gave me terrible bags under my eyes and Celia was frightened. I lost weight and my pulse even became irregular. My daughter scolded me and I gave in. I had problems every day and didn't sleep a wink. All that to get some money to move to Miami because of the climate and my wife's friends. But I wasn't going to have enough money until ten years from then. And when it'd be time to retire, I'd be a human waste and not a person. I prefer to stay here like I said because New York made me not want to leave, although it does seem ironic. Living here is how you realize that. It's a damned bug that gets inside, like a mosquito in your ear. It's also fear of the uncertain and instability.

I don't have a great salary, but it's enough to get by. My building doesn't have forty apartments, so I can't join the union. That's why my salary doesn't increase. I earn some extra money doing plumbing. I'm the neighborhood plumber. Even a Palestine family and some filthy rich Jews have called me. First impressions go a long way. As a plumber, I've seen incredible things like human bones in pipes, how do you explain that? Fetuses in tanks, dogs buried in toilets . . .

The case of Milly Carson Puyear is way up there on my list. Milly must be about seventy years old. She's supposedly a Barnard College graduate. Milly lives in 5-C. It was a good apartment and now it's a dump full of leaks. The lady took me to court six times. She accuses me of raping and kidnapping her, when she doesn't even have anything left that's good to look at. The police no longer pay any attention to her, but for years I was appearing religiously at the precinct.

She makes up everything. She says that I hit her on the stairs, bite her, and check her out. Since she's from the Appalachian Mountains, she speaks a very rough English, I can hardly understand her. She has bruises all over her body because she falls in the street in the snow and slush. So she goes to the precinct and accuses me of giving her those bruises. Three police captains and two detectives came to my house several months ago to investigate. She also accused me of selling marijuana and having a junk store as a front for drugs. The police finally have her labeled as incorrigible, but even so I've gotten a bad reputation in the neighborhood because she whines and cries and people hold a grudge against me. When she took me every week to the police, I appealed for a lawyer. As a professional, he suggested that she go to a clinic for the demented, but it was like he was speaking to a wall. She continues to do her things. She doesn't go to the trials because she loses. She doesn't have any proof. She can't invent things on the spot. Because of her I have a police record for mistreating women. It's a nightmare, but it's true. A crazy woman with two cases of child abuse on her record, accusing me of being a stalker and a potential assassin?

The police could really see how it was when I accused her of not wanting to open the door for me. I was knocking for a week and she didn't answer. I knew that she was inside, but no answer. Celia came up and said in English, "Milly, please come out," but she didn't do a thing. So I called the police, something I never do, but I had the entire building upside down. In Milly's apartment there was a very large leak that went all the way down to the basement. The water had soaked the walls of several apartments, and the people couldn't take it anymore.

"Milly Caron, open your door please." The police are something else, they don't waste any time. They knew she was inside because one of the dogs barked and she covered its mouth. Milly had two French poodles, a black one and a white one. The white one was a filthy gray and the black one was a skeleton, not a dog. When the captain gave the last kick to the door, he found piles of old clothes, newspapers, and cans piled up in the apartment. That place was a dump, not a house. Milly had become a bag lady for no reason.

She collected any old, stupid thing. The empty cans were piled to the ceiling. The refrigerator was disconnected and full of clothing and shoes. The mattress on the floor was a waste. I think she slept standing. The bathroom was the worst of all. The toilet was full of dirt and a white cross with the name "Lot" on it.

"Who's that?" the captain asked.

"It's my . . ."

And she started to cry. She had buried her black poodle in the toilet. That's why she refused to open the door. The apartment was practically flooded. They took her to the precinct while we cleaned out the place. But she's already back with her gray dog. And now her thing is to sit on the stairs and watch the neighbors. She tells them to clean the hand rail: "Don't touch the hand rail." People call me to tell me this. I go and tell her nicely, "Milly, go home," but it's like talking to a wall.

I also have a very strange Ecuadorian woman living here. She spends the entire day eating. In one hand the bag of popcorn and in the other an ice cream or a Milky Way. She's intolerable. She refuses to paint the apartment white. She doesn't pay the electricity bill. She doesn't clean the kitchen. It's disgusting! I call the real estate inspector and he blames it on me. Enough is enough, right? Miss De la Montera's last trick was to buy black paint for her place. I didn't allow that. The inspector told her that she had to change it and the next day she came to me in the basement and very politely said, "Julián, I'll give you this paint for the pipes." Two cans of black paint and a six-inch paint brush. They're totally crazy.

If I tell the story about the Cuban guy, you won't believe me! He's a braggart, *sí señor*. His name is Higinio, but they call him Tony. I don't. I call him Higinio because it bothers him. He must have arrived here in the 20s. He has brought more than fifty different women to the apartment, all prostitutes. He is, or was, sexually messed up because now he only has his head filled with a bunch of bad ideas. He got involved with a million things in this country, especially with gambling. Someone told Miguelito that he was a musician, but I don't believe it. He must've escaped from Cuba because he's a thief. He doesn't bother with me. He's also ancient. But years ago he was the disgrace of this place. He'd spend his summers in Florida and sublet the apartment without my authorization. He brought home the worst of Manhattan. He threw many parties. One night, in one of the wild parties, someone left a lit cigarette, and it burned like Troy. It was two in the morning. Thick smoke was coming out of the door. I smelled it. I immediately called the firehouses on 19th Street and I went up there with blankets and old rags. I couldn't smother the fire all by myself, but I was able to get into the apartment. A naked, very young, blond American girl was sleeping as if nothing was going on. I threw water on her face. When she woke up and saw the smoke, she started to scream. They carried her out onto the fire escape and I followed. Luckily the fire didn't destroy the walls or the floor. It did, however, destroy almost all the living room furniture.

There are many fires in this city. That explains all the iron stairs on the buildings. That's why foreigners are scared of the alarms in the houses and the fire truck sirens. You always hear them. Sometimes it's like a concert, one whistle after another without stopping. There's no peace and quiet!

I didn't get hurt that time. Luckily the fire didn't reach the basement. If those papers catch on fire one day, no one in the building will live to tell the story, no one.

Today my back hurt when I woke up. It must be from shoveling snow and carrying the garbage bags out to the sidewalk. Or perhaps it's from bending over the *boila* too long. When it's artic cold like this year, I have to stay on top of things. It could also be from opening and closing the doors too much or simply from old age, although I refuse to use my age as an excuse.

The day my Social Security kicked in, I was sad instead of happy. I was out of there with all the papers done in half an hour. The girl was very helpful. I've been lucky with Puerto Rican women. She said to me in Spanish and English, "Here you go, Honey, all of this is in order. You're all set. Okay? Have a good day!"

I went out on 6th Avenue and felt very alone even though I have my wife and daughter. I went to a café and started to think. There's a novel inside each of us. No one knows for sure how someone else feels. No two snowflakes are alike, no two men look alike. In this country I've learned many things, but the most truthful is that you can't make a home in a foreign land. That's been the biggest lesson of my life. And I figured that out on my own.

I used to like the snow. Now I hate it because it means I have to work. I've practically left Miguelito in charge of the flea market. Celia still goes because I want to get rid of all the old merchandise. There's enough here to do with the super thing. I don't feel like going out any more. Not because I hate people, that's not it. It always makes me happy to see other faces. New York is good for that. But they're strange people, everyone does their own thing. And they're always in a hurry. I go down to the subway in the rush-hour avalanche, and I feel like screaming in English, "Where are you animals going?"

They run into each other and don't even realize it. You'd think there was a fire in the station. They're going to work, to the movies, or to buy dog food. No one thinks that they can die tomorrow.

The other day at the 6th Avenue and West 4th Street station there was an old Irishman playing *La Guantanamera* on top of an oilcan. Some people made a circle around him because he was playing so well. I threw a dollar at him and the little old man looked at me. I get emotional every time I hear Cuban music. I was going to say to him in English, "I'm Cuban. Thank you," but the train came. I told Celia about it when I got home and she asked me, laughing hysterically, "Julián, aren't you tired of hearing *La Guantanamera*?"

I don't get tired of hearing Cuban music. Nor do I get tired of seeing Cuban films. If I spend a lot of time in the basement, it's because of the Cuban newspapers. I certainly can't do without them. My daughter always gets on my case when she comes to Chelsea. She says that I'm like a mouse because I don't want to come out of the basement. She's young and because she was born here, she can't understand me. But she's my daughter, and I deal with it.

Years ago a book of fables in Spanish fell into my hands and I read it all. I can't remember the author's name, but I never forgot the one fable. It's a very harsh fable, like all of them, but it's really true. It's called "Granite's Plateau." One night I read it to my daughter so that she'd teach it to my grandchildren. She said to me half in English and half in Spanish, "Come on, Pa, you always exaggerate."

But I don't exaggerate. The story is very simple. A man didn't have anything to eat so he made a hole in the ground with his hands and planted a seed. It didn't rain for weeks. So the man started to cry over the hole so that the seed wouldn't dry up. His tears fell inside the hole and within a few days one of the most beautiful sprouts appeared. Something similar has happened with the life of many men. Everything's a lot of work! For my daughter things have been a little bit easier. That's why she doesn't understand me. She hasn't stopped me from going to Cuba in any way, but she hasn't encouraged me to do so. My wife's crazy about the trip. We already filled out the papers and bought our tickets. I'm going to leave Miguelito as super because the two of us can't go together. The building can't be left in some stranger's hands. After all, it's my building and it's what supports Celia and myself.

I always dreamed about Cuba and the dream never came true. I still think I'm dreaming. It seems unreal. Just yesterday my daughter came to say goodbye to us. This year it snowed a lot and from the basement window you can see the snow falling. She came in because I had the door open. She asked me in Spanish, "Pa, what are you doing stuck to that window?"

It was snowing lightly. It looked like shaved coconut. I'm neither crazy nor blind. But because the excitement of the trip was so overwhelming, I said to her, "I'm looking at El Prado de La Habana."

"What are you talking about, Papa?"

"El Prado de La Habana, my child, the Malecón."

I felt like I was in Cuba. She didn't answer me. I didn't want to turn around. I couldn't. A man doesn't want his daughter to see him . . .

Bibliography

Coleman, Terry. *Passage to America*. London, 1972.

Colón, Jesús. *A Puerto Rican in New York, and Other Sketches*. Mainstream Publishers: NY, 1961.

Davie, Maurice R. *Passage to America*. London, 1972.

Fornet, Ambrosio. *En blanco y negro*. Instituto Cubano del Libro: La Habana, 1967.

Galíndez, Jesús de. *Puerto Rico en Nueva York*. Editorial Tiempo Contemporáneo: Argentina, 1968.

Grupo Areíto. *Contra viento y marea*. Premio Casa de las Américas. Ed. Casa: La Habana, 1978.

Handling, Oscar. *The Uprooted*. Boston, 1973.

Iglesias, César Andreú. *Memorias de Bernardo Vega*. Ediciones Huracán: San Juan, 1977.

Levine, Barry. *Benjie López*. Caribbean Review Press: Miami, 1980.

Lewis, Óscar. *La vida*. Random House: New York, 1965–1966.

Maldwin, Jones A. *Destination America*. Holt, Reinhardt and Winston: New York, 1976.

Mohr, Nicholasa. *In Nueva York*. Dell Publishing Company, Inc.: New York, 1979.

Ojeda Reyes, Félix. *Vito Marcantonio y Puerto Rico*. Ediciones Huracán: San Juan, 1978.

Solomon, Barbara. *Ancestors and Immigrants*. Cambridge, MA: 1956.

The Federal Writers Project Guide to 1930's New York: *The WPA Guide to New York City*. Pantheon Books: NY, 1939–1982.

Waganheim, Kal and Olga. *The Puertorricans*. Praeger Publishers: New York, 1973.

Zinn, Howard. *A People's History of the United States*. Harper Colophon Book: New York, 1980.

Note:

I have also reviewed the collection of the magazine *Gráfico* along with the following newspapers: *La Prensa*, *El Diario*, *El Diario de la Prensa*, and *El Imparcial*. I also consulted the following Cuban newspapers: *Diario de la Marina*, *El País*, *Avance*, and *Noticias de Hoy*.

Breinigsville, PA USA
08 October 2010
246918BV00002B/4/P